A NEW DESCRIPTION OF

SIR JOHN SOANE'S
MUSEUM

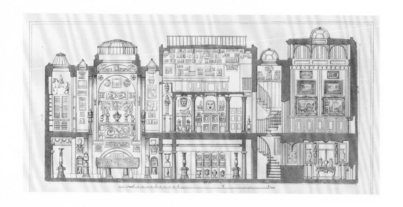

First Published 1955
Revised Edition 1966
2nd Revised Edition 1969
3rd Revised Edition 1972
4th Revised Edition 1977
5th Revised Edition 1981
6th Revised Edition 1984
7th Revised Edition 1986
8th Revised Edition 1988
9th Revised Edition 1991
10th Revised and fully illustrated Edition 2001
11th Revised Edition 2007

Supported by
MLA Designation
Challenge Fund

Registered Charity Number 313609
ISBN: 978-0-9549041-7-3

Designed and typeset by Libanus Press, Marlborough
Printed by B·A·S Printers, Romsey

Front cover: Detail of the Dome Area *Photograph: Martin Charles*
Back cover: Detail of the façade, 13 Lincoln's Inn Fields *Photograph: Richard Bryant/Arcaid*
Half-title illustration: Section through the Museum, engraving, from *The Union of Architecture,*
Sculpture and Painting by John Britton, 1827 *Photograph: Geremy Butler*
Page iii, opposite: Sir John Soane by William Owen, 1805 *Photograph: Geremy Butler*

A NEW DESCRIPTION OF
SIR JOHN SOANE'S
MUSEUM

PUBLISHED BY THE TRUSTEES

CONTENTS

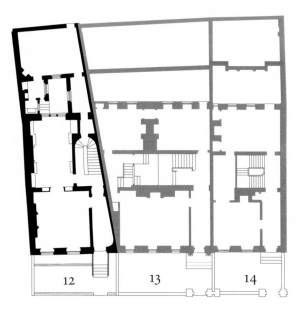

Plan of the ground floors of Nos 12, 13 & 14 Lincoln's Inn Fields as existing about the year 1796 (area outlined in bold indicates the extent of Soane's rebuilding at this date)

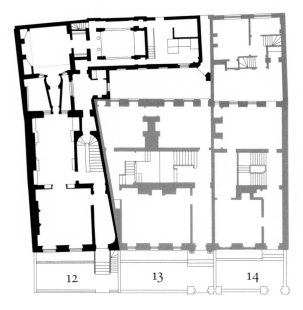

Plan of the ground floors of Nos 12, 13 & 14 Lincoln's Inn Fields as existing about the year 1810

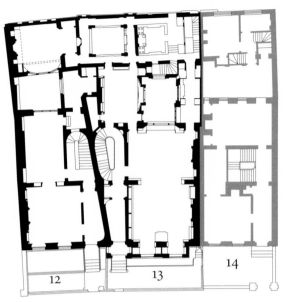

Plan of the ground floors of Nos 12, 13 & 14 Lincoln's Inn Fields as existing about the year 1822

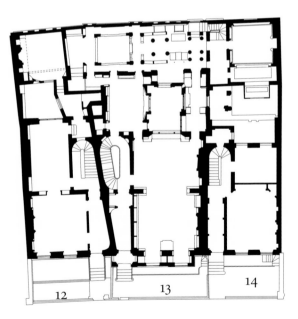

Plan of the ground floors of Nos 12, 13 & 14 Lincoln's Inn Fields as existing about the year 1837

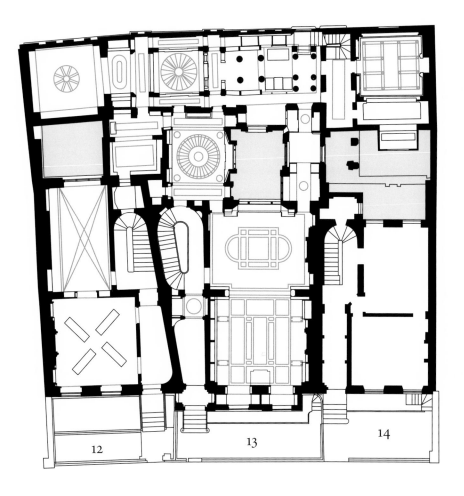

12

13

14

N

| 0 | 10 | 20 | 30 | 40 | 50 feet |

| 0 | 5 | 10 | 15 metres |

Plan of the ground floors of Nos 12, 13 & 14 Lincoln's Inn Fields at present

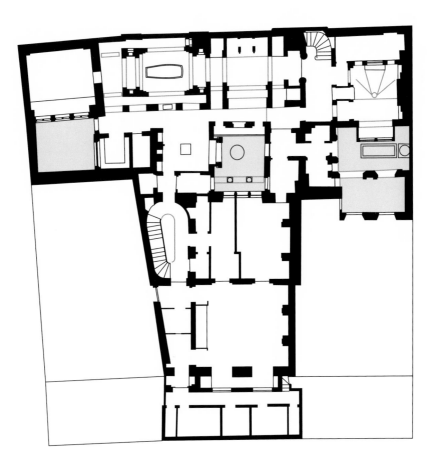

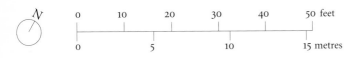

Basement plan of the Museum as at present

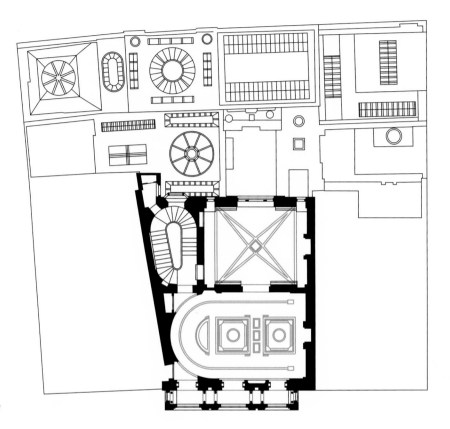

First floor plan of the Museum as at present

No. 13 Lincoln's Inn Fields.
The top storey was added by Soane in 1825.
Photograph: Martin Charles

PREFACE TO THE ELEVENTH EDITION

This new guidebook – the eleventh edition of the *New Description* – is a detailed account of Sir John Soane's Museum and its collections, serving as the *vade mecum* or essential companion for all who wish to understand Soane's extraordinary creation, from the casual visitor to the serious student.

Since the publication of the last edition of this guide in 2001, various historic features in the Museum have been reinstated to their appearance in Sir John's day. Perhaps the most dramatic improvement is the restoration of the Three Courtyards, carried out by my predecessor, Mrs Margaret Richardson, between 2001 and 2005, with the help of a generous grant from the Heritage Lottery Fund. Although the works encompassed the restoration of the entire basement of the Museum, by far the most spectacular change was the reconstruction of Soane's lost 'Pasticcio' in the Monument Court, a 23-foot high folly composed of architectural salvage which Soane intended as a monumental tribute to the development of architectural styles through the ages. The restoration of the Monk's Yard, completed under my own direction between 2005 and 2006, involved the consolidation of 'ruins' composed of fragments of Gothic stonework from the old Palace of Westminster and the reinstatement of Soane's curious pavement of pebbles and bottle tops and bottoms.

Another improvement carried out in the last two years is the remedying of serious structural failure in the fabric to the rear of the Museum, particularly in the Museum Corridor outside Soane's famous Picture Room. As well as consolidating the precarious brickwork, the opportunity was taken to remove a late nineteenth-century iron and glass industrial pavement, and reinstate Soane's original floor of York stone pierced by iron grilles. Now visitors can enjoy the sombre effect of light filtering through the grilles to the gloomy crypts beneath, just as Soane intended. Indeed, light levels have been lowered throughout the Museum to emphasise the contrasts between light and shade that Soane so enjoyed exploiting in his buildings.

When he set up his Museum in 1833, Soane left strict instructions that his arrangements should be preserved exactly as he left them and subsequent curators of the Museum have generally respected his wish, making Sir John Soane's Museum a unique survival – the intact house and collections of one of the greatest architects of the Regency era. However, a few well-meaning changes were made, largely for practical reasons, in the mid- to late nineteenth century, and these are almost always to the detriment of Soane's original vision. Therefore, it has been the objective of successive curators of this Museum to reverse these changes and return to Soane's arrangements. Many casts and items of sculpture have recently been returned to their original positions throughout the Museum, notably in the Museum Corridor and around the sarcophagus in the Crypt, as part of this ongoing policy of returning the Museum to its appearance in 1837.

But by far the most important change to the Soane Museum since the last edition of the *New Description* is the opening of the next door house, No. 14 Lincoln's Inn Fields. Acquired in 1996 with the assistance of the Heritage Lottery Fund, the Museum gained possession of this fine Soane-designed townhouse in 2003 at the expiry of the commercial lease. After years of fundraising, the house has been restored by Julian Harrap Architects in 2006–07 and now provides the Museum with dedicated education facilities for children, a seminar room for lectures and meetings, a new research library and staff offices. Never lived in or furnished by Soane himself, many of its original features have been restored or reinstated. The new facilities in No. 14 will, in due course, enable the Museum to restore and open to the public Soane's private apartments on the second floor of the Museum, which were dismantled in the 1840s and have been used as staff offices ever since. The Museum is currently undertaking a major fundraising campaign to embark upon this work of restoration, which will enable us to show eight additional Soane rooms to the public, together with a wealth of historic contents, including Soane's celebrated collection of architectural models. This ambitious project – known as the Soane Museum Masterplan – will also improve visitor reception and circulation, provide a proper cloakroom, a new Soane Gallery, and a better shop – essential facilities for a Museum that now welcomes over 90,000 visitors every year, free of charge just as Sir John Soane wished. What will not change, however, is the unique atmosphere of this most charming of all historic house museums.

Tim Knox
DIRECTOR
July 2007

Fig. 1: opposite: The Dome Area
Photograph: Martin Charles

DESCRIPTION OF
THE HOUSE AND MUSEUM

Fig. 2: The Entrance Hall and staircase
Photograph: Richard Bryant/Arcaid

THE ENTRANCE FRONT

The entrance to the Museum is at No. 13 Lincoln's Inn Fields, the middle house of three built by Sir John Soane. He built No. 12 in 1792, No. 13 in 1812 and No. 14 in 1824. No. 13 is the Museum proper and connects with buildings at the rear extending behind Nos 12 and 14. No. 12 was Soane's residence for 19 years from 1794 to 1813, after which date he let it on lease. At his death he left it in trust as part of his endowment; the rental income to fund the Museum. It was re-occupied by the Trustees as an extension of the Museum in 1969. After Soane re-built No. 14 he did not occupy the main front part of the house himself. It was leased out and on his death passed in trust to his family. However, Soane retained the rear premises of No. 14, including the courtyard, using these to build the Picture Room, Monk's Parlour and Monk's Yard.

Nos 12 and 14 are of white brick with Portland stone dressings. No. 13 (the Museum) is of brick and Portland stone, the stone portion consisting of a 'verandah' (or 'loggia') projecting in front of the building line. This was originally open but the openings were glazed by Soane in 1829 and 1834, when the verandah became part of the internal space. The top storey was added by Soane in 1825, an addition that considerably altered the proportions of the façade.

At second-floor level are two figures in Coade Stone, free versions of the caryatids at the Erechtheion in Athens. Soane thought of them as counterparts of two classical figures which stood on the façade of the College of Surgeons nearly opposite, on the south side of Lincoln's Inn Fields (now entirely rebuilt except for the portico colums). The Gothic pedestals built into the piers, between the windows, come from the 14th-century north front of Westminster Hall where they formed pedestals in the niches on either side of the entrance. They were inserted into the façade in 1825, (see illustration p.xii).

THE GROUND FLOOR

The hall has walls '*which are coloured to imitate porphyry. The ceiling of the Hall is connected with the walls by a small cove and is enriched with three roses in plaster, after the antique*'. On the walls are circular plaques (nine in all) of terracotta or patent stone, representing Classical subjects. They were made and fixed in 1833.

In an opening in the north-west corner of the outer hall is a marble bust of Sir Thomas Lawrence, the painter, by R W Sievier, who presented it to Soane. It is a posthumous bust, exhibited at the Royal Academy in the year of Lawrence's death,

1830 (see p.61). Over it is a cast of '*a beautiful female torso found at Capua*' in the 18th century and now in the Museo Nazionale at Naples. Over the arch is a model of an ornamental feature designed by Soane for the top of cupboards in the Bank of England.

The ceiling rose in the dome of the inner hall is based on an original in the soffit of the portico of the Temple of Mars Ultor at Rome and was originally painted bronze green.

The folding doors (1908) and the fanlight (original) above them contain panels of ancient glass. These include three lozenge-shaped English medieval quarries. The rest of the panels are Netherlandish or German of the 16th, 17th or early 18th century.

From the inner hall you pass to the staircase, which, owing to a peculiarity of the site, with a sloping party wall between Nos 12 and 13 Lincoln's Inn Fields, widens towards the far end. The stair is a stone cantilever or 'geometrical' stair with wrought-iron balustrade and a hand-rail of laminated mahogany in runs of from five to nine feet. The walls are painted in imitation of *giallo antico* marble and are now much darker than they were in Soane's day. Soane's original marbling was painted over in the late 19th century and the current marbled finish is a re-creation dating from 1925.

THE DINING ROOM AND LIBRARY

Soane considered these as '*one room, being separated only by two projecting piers formed into bookcases, from which springs a canopy composed of three segmental Arches*'. This 'open plan' made it possible to extend the dining-table (by adding leaves) into the Library area, when a larger number of guests were to be entertained. The 'canopy', as originally constructed and prior to 1832, consisted of three semi-circular arches (see Fig.5). Similar 'canopies' are deployed over the bookcases on the east and west walls of the Library. The recesses behind them are fitted with mirror-glass reflecting the arches and ceiling. Mirrors are also introduced over the fireplace in the Dining Room and in the jambs and mullions of the window looking into the Monument Court. The style of these rooms is peculiar to Soane though the decorations probably owe something to coloured engravings of Roman frescoes found in the grounds of the Villa Negroni, some of which hang in the Breakfast Parlour (p.72).

Starting at the fireplace in the Dining Room, we see over it the portrait of Soane by Sir Thomas Lawrence, '*almost the last picture painted by that distinguished artist*'. Soane was sitting for the portrait in 1828 and it was completed in the following year. Below the portrait, on the chimney-piece, is a model of the Board of Trade and Privy Council Offices, Whitehall, as proposed by Soane in 1822 or a little later, with a Triumphal Arch leading into Downing Street and the façade repeated southwards (see p.32). Only part of the northern (right-hand) section was built and this was remodelled by Sir Charles Barry to form the

Fig. 3: Detail of the west side of the Library *Photograph: Martin Charles*

Treasury in 1846–47 (now the Cabinet Office). '*The buildings in this design are so arranged, that when completed, a view of the north entrance into Westminster Abbey Church would be obtained from Whitehall.*'

Proceeding to the right, from the fireplace, we come to the projecting pedestal under the 'canopy' which divides the rooms. Here is an Apulian amphora of the late 4th c. BC, bought at the sale of Sir Henry Englefield's collection in 1823.

On either side of this pedestal are small bronzes. *Left:* Napoleon after Canova and a vase in the form of a grotesque head, origin unknown. *Right:* Napoleon as First Consul and a bust of William Dodd, DD, poet and essayist, executed for forgery, 1777.

'*On the east side of the library, over the chimney-piece, upon the cornice of the bookcases, springs a large flat Arch, forming a recess; and to connect the symmetry, there are two semicircular Arches: over the chimney-piece is a large Looking-glass, with some small Figures by Tassie.*' These 'Figures by Tassie' are above the mirror and take the form of a bas-relief after the antique. To the left and right of this are bas-reliefs by John Flaxman, 'The Silver Age' and 'The Golden Age' (inspired by texts in Hesiod), placed here in the last months of Soane's life. Above the book-cases are '*several Etruscan vases* [they are in fact Greek colonial wares], *rich in form and decoration, and also a specimen of Wedgwood's imitation of Etruscan pottery*' known as 'black basaltes' ware.

The two armchairs (bergères) date from about 1830 and the foot-stools from slightly later. The day-bed was almost certainly supplied by John Robins of Warwick Street, Golden Square, a London upholsterer who carried out much work for Soane at the Bank of England and elsewhere. He certainly made the bookcases in this room and the dining chairs. Against the pier stands an elegant library-table which Soane must have designed and which Robins may have executed. In 1812 Soane had it brought from his residence at Chelsea Hospital to be placed in this room, although in the 1790s it stood in his Breakfast Room at No. 12 Lincoln's Inn Fields (see p.68). Soane designed a house in Park Lane and business premises in Regent Street for Robins.

On the pier-table stands an Astronomical Clock, with amboyna wood and ormolu mounts, by Raingo, of Paris, *c.*1820. Formerly the property of Frederick, Duke of York, it was bought by Soane in the year of the Duke's death, 1827, for £75. Five of these clocks are known to have been in existence in recent years. There is one (almost identical to our example) in Queen Elizabeth's Gallery at Windsor Castle. Another, in private ownership, has a musical box in its base.

At the south end of the room two arches open into what was originally (until 1829) an open loggia, where Soane installed '*an ornamental pump, supplied with*

Fig. 4: The ceiling paintings in the Dining Room by Henry Howard, RA
Photograph: Martin Charles

excellent water from a well in the basement story'. 'Between the piers at this end of the room are two deep recesses, surrounded with bookcases surmounted with busts of Homer, Shakespeare, Camden, Napoleon and Inigo Jones and terminated with two windows, the internal surface of the shutters to which are faced with looking-glass.' These sliding shutters faced internally with mirror-glass, together with the pier-glass between the windows, present an essentially uninterrupted sheet of mirror across the south end of the room when the shutters are closed.

The west side of the room corresponds in design to the east, though with a continuous range of bookcases in the absence of the fireplace. Note the narrow strips of mirror-glass between each bookcase. On the projecting pedestal is a model of the tomb which Soane erected for his wife in 1816, in the Burial Ground of St Giles-in-the-Fields (now St Pancras Gardens, see p.148 & Fig.3), in which he and his eldest son John are also buried. The model is inscribed *'Chere aimé, je ne peux plus entendre ta voix – apprends moi ce que je dois faire – pour remplir tes souhaits!'* (Dear friend, I can no longer hear your voice – teach me what I must do to fulfill your wishes). An identical inscription hangs beneath the portrait of Mrs Soane in the South Drawing Room (p.77).

The chairs against the west wall were made in China (Canton), probably in the 1720s, after designs that were undoubtedly sent out from England. They are of padouk wood (a type of rosewood) inlaid with mother-of-pearl. They bear the arms of Sir Gregory Page (d.1775), of Wricklemarsh, near Blackheath, impaled with those of his wife, Martha, third daughter of Robert Kenward, Esq., of Yalding, Kent, whom he married in 1721. The chairs came from Wricklemarsh, which was sold by his nephew and heir, Sir G Page Turner, in 1783. Soane seems to have purchased them in 1787 when a payment of £178 1s is recorded to 'Sir Gregory Page'.

On the west side of the Dining Room is the painting 'Love and Beauty' by Sir Joshua Reynolds. Alternatively known as 'The Snake in the Grass', this painting was in the collection of Reynolds' niece, Mary Palmer, who became Marchioness of Thomond, and was bought by Soane for 510 gns when the collection was sold in 1821. It is a version of the painting exhibited by Reynolds at the Royal Academy in 1784 under the title 'A Nymph and Cupid', and now in the Tate Gallery. There is another version in the State Hermitage Museum, St Petersburg. Below the painting is a sideboard on which stand two knife-boxes, and a silver tureen presented to Soane in 1795 by his friend Rowland Burdon, in gratitude for

Fig. 5: The Dining Room on 29 October 1825, watercolour by J M Gandy *Photograph: Ole Woldbye*

his help over the construction of Wearmouth Bridge.

Turning to the north, there is a large window flanked with mirror-glass, and *'enriched with scriptural subjects on glass'*. The stained glass including two large panels depicting the Creation and the Last Judgement (Swiss, *c.*1600), was badly damaged in 1940, but rescued and stored. The panels have now been restored and replaced in their original positions. *'From this window'*, says Soane, *'the Monument Court, with its Architectural Pasticcio, and assemblage of ancient and modern Art, and particularly the Frieze of Grecian sculpture, are seen to great advantage. The lovers of Grecian art will be gratified by comparing the outline of this work with the two natural productions on the sides of the window, found growing in the hollow of an old oak pollard.'* The 'pasticcio', a composite column made up of ancient and modern architectural fragments, erected in 1819 in the centre of the courtyard, became dangerous and was removed in 1896 but has now been reconstructed incorporating the surviving sections. The curved 'Grecian frieze', seen behind the 18th-century statue of Paris on the roof, is actually a Roman fragment, bought by Soane at the Bessborough sale of 1801. Two 'natural productions' hang on the outer jambs of the window; the Inventory of 1837 describes them as 'part of a branch of an ash tree, from the woods of Stainstead Park near Emsworth, Sussex'.

The objects seen in the Monument Court are mostly fragments salvaged from buildings demolished in Soane's time. Thus, the term, and the capital below, of Anglo-Flemish character, on the left-hand (west) wall, came from Furnival's Inn, Holborn, a mid-17th-century building demolished in 1818. Other fragments recall the styles of William Kent and Robert Adam, while others again are specimens of ornaments prepared for Soane's Bank of England. On the skyline to the north are two ammonite fossils flanking, in the centre, a terracotta bust of the Farnese Hercules. On the parapet on the east side is a Coade Stone urn from Carlton House.

In the window stand a pair of 18th-century Italian marble vases formerly belonging to the miniaturist Richard Cosway, RA, a pair of jars of Egyptian alabaster, and two very large green Chinese porcelain vases on stands, given to Soane by Viscount Bridport, whose house at Cricket in Somerset he had built. In the centre of the window sill stands a large Apulian crater of the late 4th century BC, acquired by Soane at the sale of Lord Cawdor's collection in 1800. According to Michaelis, the 'Cawdor Vase' was found in 1790 at Lecce and was for some years in the possession of the King of Naples. It was then purchased by General Oudinot, sent to England and subsequently sold for 1,000 gns to Lord Cawdor. Soane bought it for £68 5s. Soane pointed out that *'The effect of these works is considerably heightened by the looking-glass in the splayed jambs of the windows'.*

In high-level niches round the room are busts cast from antique examples and supposed to represent Geta, Plautilla, Faustina, Sappho, Dione and Flora. They are curiously reflected in the convex mirrors placed alongside.

The dining-table is late 18th-century and can be extended with extra leaves. The trellis-back chairs were provided by Robins (see p.6) in 1821 and are similar to those made, also under Soane's direction, for the Governor's Suite in the Bank of England. The two armchairs are of slightly earlier date.

The ceiling of the Library and Dining Room is decorated with pictures by Henry Howard, RA (Fig.4) These were commissioned in 1834 and completed only shortly before Soane died. The story of Pandora and her vase *'whence . . . issued all the cares and miseries of life'* is the subject of the pictures over the Dining Room. It has been suggested that the figure of Night, in a black veil, in the second panel from the fireplace, may be based on Mrs Soane. Over the Library ceiling *'surrounded by paintings of Architectural decorations, is represented Phoebus in his car, preceded by Aurora and the Morning Star, led on by the Hours'.*

In 1823 Soane bought three Axminster carpets to cover the floor of the two rooms but leaving a border of exposed floorboards all round. He paid £81 15s for the three carpets and two hearth rugs. This was conspicuous expenditure as this was the most expensive form of English carpet available. Such carpets were usually made specially to order. Replicas of the original carpets (which are too fragile to be walked on) were laid in 2005.

THE LITTLE STUDY

The Study and adjoining Dressing Room (see p.13) were very personal to Soane. Here he must have executed preliminary sketches for his architectural schemes and, in the Dressing Room, he could tidy himself in preparation for meeting builders and specialist contractors who would have entered the house through the office door on to Whetstone Park. The doorways were widened towards the end of the last century but have now (with the exception of the entrance from the Dining Room) been narrowed again to their original widths (1990). The shelf across the window, with its decorative ornaments on the underside, displays a *'large fungus from the rocks of the island of Sumatra . . .* [which] *will be appreciated by the lovers of natural history'.* The 'fungus' is in fact a Neptune's Cup Sponge. Note the small table on castors which slides into the knee-hole of the desk under the window. This was made specially for this position in April 1818 by Thomas Martyr and may be extended by a flap at the back when pulled out. Soane almost certainly worked on a quarto drawing board at this table. The two brass grilles in the floor were for hot air to pass into the room from the central heating system; there was a stove in the basement. The skylight is filled with coloured glass, alternating primrose yellow and dark yellow.

This room contains a large number of antique marble fragments, nearly all from the collection put together by Charles Heathcote Tatham (1772–1842) in Rome in the years 1794–96, on behalf of the architect Henry Holland, whose

Fig. 6: The Study looking south towards the Dining Room *Photograph: Martin Charles*

pupil he was. They date from the time of the Roman Empire and all appear to have come originally from sites in Rome or those of neighbouring Imperial villas. Sometime after Holland's death (1806) the collection came into Soane's possession, probably in 1812 (see also p.99). His notebook records that he was 'arranging marbles' in the Study in 1816 and two watercolours of 1817, made by Soane's pupils, show the Tatham pieces in position. In January 1822 Soane was again 'arranging marbles' in the Study and seems to have continued altering and perfecting his display right up to his death.

Some of the most important antique fragments from the Tatham collection are displayed around the chimney-piece on the east wall. The most notable is the portion of a Roman altar or statue group base with bulls' heads and garlands, dating from the first half of the first century AD. Tatham noted on his drawing of this piece that it was 'in the possession of Signor Angelo Grimaschi, Sculptor at Rome [who] demanded 20 Scudi [for it]'. Another fragment of the same work with a bull's head and honeysuckle ornament is shown directly above. To the left on the chimney-piece is a very fine early Roman imperial period carved acroterion and to the right a fragment of a Roman pilaster panel showing foliage, birds and a vase. The other fragments include architectural enrichments and parts of candelabra. The four cinerary urns (1st and 2nd centuries AD) in recesses near the floor were bought by Soane at sales in 1801–02.

Over the doorway leading into the Dining Room is a cast of 'The Apotheosis of Homer', from the original marble, formerly in Palazzo Colonna, Rome, but purchased by the British Museum in 1819. There is another cast of the same subject in the Basement Ante-Room (p.44). The two large reliefs (2nd century AD) on either side of the doorway ('*a delicious antique fragment in the true gusto antico*') are perhaps fragments of a statue base. Between the doorway and the window are some plaques and reliefs. These include an ivory head of Inigo Jones, probably bought from Edward Burch, and a 17th-century Italian wax relief, probably showing the bodies of Count Ugolino and his sons as well as '*Paws of Animals, of extraordinary execution*'.

Above the doorway opposite, to the north, is a marble panel with scroll ornament (probably North Italian, 15th-century). On either side of the doorway are bronze statuettes on pedestals (probably German or Flemish, early 17th-century). Beneath them are mahogany racks for visiting cards, invitations etc. To the left of the doorway are more antique fragments from the Tatham collection and some plaster medallions depicting Greek gods designed by James Tassie.

The central rose in the ceiling is a cast copied from one of the enrichments in the frieze of the Temple of Vespasian, Rome. The other fragments on the ceiling are marble and from the Tatham collection. The asymmetrical arrangement on the ceiling is the result of the fact that the skylight was extended by two bays during Soane's lifetime.

THE DRESSING ROOM

To the left and right of the entry to this room are glass-fronted cupboards, originally bookcases but now filled with miscellaneous small objects of art removed from their original positions for various reasons.

The left-hand (west) cupboard contains antique fragments, chiefly from the Tatham collection. The following are especially noteworthy: top shelf: a bearded head of Dionysius, Roman 1st–2nd century AD but in the Greek 5th-century manner (left); a Roman personage of the early Flavian period, 69–96 AD (right). Middle shelf: the 'Soane Painter' vase, a Campanian (S. Italian) bell krater of the 4th century BC. A fragment of della Robbia ware (15th-century Florentine glazed terracotta) may be seen at the back of the case.

In the right-hand cupboard, the following are noteworthy: top shelf: white stoneware jug from Siegburg in the Rhineland dated 1593, said to have been discovered when digging the foundations of a house at Bath, and two vessels of English 15th- or 16th-century manufacture, probably found in similar circumstances in London. Middle shelf: important terracotta figure by Giovanni Bandini – the model for his statue of Architecture on the tomb of Michelangelo in Santa Croce, Florence, 1568. This figure retains its original painted surface which many such terracottas have lost. A bronze figure of Hercules, Italian, 16th-century. A terracotta figure of a River God, English, 18th-century, by John Bacon the elder. A maiolica plate made in Urbino at the Guido Durantino workshop in 1535 for the Montmorency family at the French château of Écouen. Bottom shelf: bronze bull, purchased at the Richard Cosway sale (1821), in the catalogue for which it is described as 'the Bull breaking the egg' (the alabaster pedestal bears the arms of the Trapani family of Sicily). Antique bronze triform Diana, probably made for use in a household shrine, also bought at the Cosway sale. In 1835 this, along with the bronze bull, stood on the chimney-piece in the Study.

The Dressing Room, finished throughout in oak-graining (restored 1953), is lit by two windows, 'one commanding a view of the ruins of the Monk's Monastery, and the other looking into the Monument Court'. The ceiling, elaborately enriched, has a lantern in the centre, the upper part of which is a model of 'the domical light in the new Masonic Hall of the Freemasons', built by Soane in 1828–30. The model seems to have been installed first in the ceiling of the Lobby beyond, leading from the Dressing Room to the Colonnade but was then moved by Soane to its present position c.1832. The ceiling as a whole, which is in Soane's late manner, probably dates from this time.

On the wall facing the entrance from the Study, above the doorway, is an aperture through to the narrow passage beyond. This aperture was blocked up after Soane's death and re-opened in 1990. To left and right of this are drawings of Baronscourt, Ireland, as remodelled by Soane for the Marquess of Abercorn, 1791–92. Below, to the left and right, are pen-and-ink drawings of 'Banditti' by J H Mortimer. Below these are two engravings by Hogarth, designed as sub-scription tickets for the sets of engravings of 'A Rake's Progress' and 'Modern Midnight Coversation'.

To the right (east) the window looks into the Monk's Yard. The yellow-coloured glass, there in Soane's day, was put back in 1990–91. To the left of this window are an engraving, 'Landscape with Bridge', by the brothers Both (Dutch, 17th-century); a plan of the drains in No. 13 Lincoln's Inn Fields c.1825 and a drawing of an Italian street scene by Canaletto.

Above the entrance from the Study is a drawing by Henry Parke of the Soane tomb in the Burial Ground of St Giles-in-the-Fields (see also pages 7, 71 and 148). This originally hung on the door (now missing) between the Study and the Dressing Room, as did Soane's design for a 'Canine Residence' or classical dog-kennel, made for the Bishop of Derry and dated *Romae 1778* which now hangs on the west wall to the right of the window. Also above the entrance from the Study is a pencil portrait of Maria Denman, by her brother-in-law, the sculptor John Flaxman. On the shelf are two models of attics for the Bank of England, and one for the lodge at Tyringham.

To the left of the doorway is a water-colour portrait by Clara Maria Pope of

Fig. 7: Giovanni Bandini, terracotta model for the figure of 'Architecture' on Michelangelo's tomb in the church of Santa Croce, Florence *Photograph: Ole Woldbye*

Fig. 8: Portrait of Maria Denman
by John Flaxman
Photograph: Geremy Butler

Miss Norah Brickenden, a friend of Soane in his later years. Below this, to
the left and right of the doorway, are four frames containing sulphur casts from
gems; the two above contain work by Edward Burch, those below, work by
Nathaniel Marchant (see below).

The window to the west looks into the Monument Court. On the shelf below
the window lie a pair of bronze stirrups which appear to be Italian 16th-century
items but which Soane was told were found on the banks of the River Boyne in
Northern Ireland and a bronze figure of Venus (probably 17th-century Italian)
which was used by Soane as a finial on a pump he installed in the front loggia of
the house (see p.6).

The pump, washbasin and casing and shelves have been recreated (1990),
following exactly an engraving of 1835 showing the Dressing Room in great detail.

In the short passage (or 'recess') leading from the Dressing Room into the
Museum are 18th-century busts, in lead, of Palladio and Inigo Jones. The circular
bell-light above this recess was described by Soane's friend the novelist Mrs
Hofland in 1835 as producing light 'of that soft primrose hue so peculiarly adapted
for the exhibition of marbles'. The door to the left leads into Soane's watercloset.

On the door leading to the Museum are hung, as they were in Soane's day,
a portrait of Nathaniel Marchant attributed to Hugh Douglas Hamilton and 'A
Scene from Macbeth' by R Westall. After passing through this door you will find
two openings to your right into the Museum Corridor.

To left of opening: two frames containing fragments of terracotta architectural reliefs (Roman).

To right of opening: fragments of a Roman imitation of an Attic relief. Below: relief, perhaps Roman, of a fleece hanging on a tree.

THE MUSEUM CORRIDOR

This 'corridor', formed when the Picture Room was built in 1824, contains a variety of antique marbles and casts. It is *'lighted in a manner to show the objects on the walls to the greatest advantage'* with its large half-round skylight filled with yellow glass. To the right of the door to the Picture Room is a recess containing *'a magnificent Fragment of Grecian Sculpture'* (in fact the shaft of a Roman fountain with vestiges of the figure of a nymph, probably from the Emperor Hadrian's villa at Tivoli, 1st–2nd century AD). Behind this hangs a terracotta relief 'Britannia attended by Peace and Plenty' by John Bacon the elder, *c*.1775 (see Fig.10). The marbles are mostly from the Tatham collection (see p.11), though the black marble Egyptian capital on the west wall was bought at the sale of Robert Adam's collection in 1818. Among the most interesting of the other fragments on the west wall is a section of the lower part of a rare version of the statue of the Ephesian Diana (numbered 63). At the foot of the staircase is a fragment

Fig. 9: The Corridor looking south, watercolour by J M Gandy, 1825
Photograph: Geremy Butler

of a Roman child's sarcophagus, showing a chariot race of cupids in the Circus.

Among the casts, important Greek and Roman temples are represented. Thus high up on the east wall is a capital from the Erechtheion while the Temple of Castor and Pollux at Rome (known to Soane as the Temple of Jupiter Stator) is represented by the great capital at the south end of the Corridor and the cornice above. Other details from this temple, as well as from the frieze of the Temple of Vespasian (called by Soane the Temple of Jupiter Tonans) and from the Temples of Vesta at Tivoli and of Mars Ultor at Rome, are on the north, east and west walls. On the west wall, to left and right of the doorway, are two casts of the label stops which were once either side of the Great South Window in Westminster Hall: the only casts in existence of these lost originals. Both depict the badge of Richard II, the White Hart, couchant within a palisade, supporting a shield bearing the royal arms (in the left-hand example the arms are those of King Edward the Confessor).

On the floor, to the left of the doorway in the west wall, is a Roman relief of a griffin, the end panel of a sarcophagus (probably late 2nd century AD).

Through the casement window at the south end of the Corridor is '*a view into the Monk's Room, which displays some powerful effects of light and shade,*

Fig. 11: The Students' Room or Upper Drawing Office *Photograph: Ole Woldbye*

and a rich assemblage of interesting objects'. In front of the window, on its original wooden stand is *'a beautiful statue, by Thomas Banks, RA, of a young female reposing on a mattress'*, the model for the tomb of Penelope Boothby at Ashbourne in Derbyshire (1791–93). The tomb is considered to be one of Banks' masterpieces: when it was exhibited at the Royal Academy in 1793 Queen Charlotte was moved to tears.

The grilles set into the stone floor allow light to filter through to the basement beneath.

THE STUDENTS' ROOM OR UPPER DRAWING OFFICE

The staircase at the north end of the corridor leads to the Students' Room, which Soane describes as *'well lighted, and peculiarly adapted for study.... The place is surrounded with the marble Fragments and Casts, from the remains of antiquity, and from the Artists of the cinquecento; and the drawers are filled with architectural drawings and prints, for the instruction of the pupils'*. (These drawings are now in the Research Library.) The room was originally Soane's Upper Drawing Office (the Lower Drawing Office lay immediately below in what is now the Colonnade). It was installed in 1821 and then altered by Soane in 1824. The room is curiously constructed, independently of the main walls, so that the two long skylights which light the drawing-tables also illuminate the exhibits on the walls down to ground-floor level and even give a ray of light (on the north side) to the Crypt. *'At the west end'* notes Soane, *'is an aperture, affording a bird's-eye view of part of the Museum.'* There is another aperture in the floor at the east end, protected by an iron railing. Over it hangs a model of the ceiling of Soane's Court of King's Bench (1823). On the shelf at the west end is a patent model for a method of laying sewers. Attached to the ceiling above is a large model of the vestibule at Bentley Priory (built by Soane in 1798). On the drawing-tables are various cases to hold drawing instruments. Soane's own drawing instruments can be seen in the larger of the two display cases on the left-hand table. The small display case contains a set of Nairne and Blunt drawing instruments, dating from the early 1790s, such as Soane might have owned. This set was purchased by the Museum in 1989.

The casts arranged round the room are mostly of small architectural details from Roman temples. Like the rest of Soane's collection of casts of such material, they served as models or sources of inspiration for the draughtsmen and assistants in his large architectural practice.

For structural reasons this room can only be visited by a few people at a time. Regrettably, therefore, it can only be seen by special arrangement.

THE PICTURE ROOM

This room was built in 1824, when Soane was 71, and thus illustrates the last phase of his style. Both the ceiling and the fireplace are curious examples of his endeavour to merge Classical and Gothic themes into a single architectural language. Note particularly what he called the 'arched canopies' of the ceiling and the 'Early English' foliage combined with Roman enrichments (from an engraving in Philibert De L'Orme's treatise on architecture of 1576) in the marble mantelpiece. The great peculiarity of the room lies in the fact that three of the walls contain hinged panels which open to display further pictures. This device is described by its inventor as follows:

'On the north and west sides of this room are cabinets; and on the south are movable planes, with sufficient space between for pictures. By this arrangement, the small space of 13ft 8in. in length, 12ft 4in. in breadth, and 19ft 6in. in height, which are the actual dimensions of this room, is rendered capable of containing as many pictures as a gallery of the same height, 20ft broad and 45ft long. Another advantage to this arrangement is that the pictures may be seen under different angles of vision.'

The dwarf bookcases which run round the room are of mahogany inlaid with ebony and were made by John Robins. The veneers and the brasswork were considered exceptionally fine when new. New doors had to be made in 1987 to replace two that were missing. One is fitted with glass as it was in Soane's day, so that light can penetrate to the Monk's Cell in the Basement via a lightshaft.

The room was re-decorated in 1988 to re-create Soane's original colour-scheme following evidence from paint-sections and numerous watercolour views of the room in Soane's time. Many of the picture-frames have been re-gilded or have had later layers of gilding and dark varnish removed to reveal the original gilded surface. Soane had frames re-gilded regularly throughout his life, on one occasion, in 1833–34, purchasing 784 books of gold leaf. The brass shelf and other fittings were meant to be kept bright and now give an indication of how the picture frames above were intended to look.

The most important pictures now in this room are the two great series by William Hogarth, 'A Rake's Progress' and 'An Election'. The eight episodes of 'A Rake's Progress' hang on the east wall. The four 'Election' pictures hang in pairs on the outer planes of the north and south cabinets. The 'Election' paintings retain their original Rococo frames, restored in 1987–88. During the restoration it was found that most of the original gilding survived under layers of varnish and new gilding was therefore applied only to areas where the original had been lost and was toned in to match it.

Fig. 12: The Picture Room, watercolour by J M Gandy, *c.*1830 (note the cork model of the Temple of Vesta at Tivoli and the Indian ivory furniture, see p.63)
Photograph: Geremy Butler

Fig. 13: The Picture Room looking east *Photograph: Richard Bryant/Arcaid*

Fig. 14: The Count of Ravenna
by Henry Fuseli, oil on canvas,
*c.*1780 *Photograph: Prudence
Cuming Associates*

A RAKE'S PROGRESS

Hogarth painted 'A Rake's Progress' in 1733–34, immediately following upon 'A
Harlot's Progress', to which it is in some respects analogous. The paintings were
produced in preparation for the engravings based on them which were published
in 1735. Potential subscribers could visit Hogarth's studio to see the paintings
before deciding whether or not to buy the engravings. Mrs Soane bid for the
paintings at a sale of William Beckford's pictures at Christie's in February 1802,
securing them for £570. Starting with the left-hand picture in the upper row the
contents of the series may be summarized as follows:

I. *The Heir* (Fig.15). Tom Rakewell on the death of his miserly father comes into
his inheritance. He is being measured for his suit of mourning, whilst his lawyer is
taking advantage of his back being turned to rob him. The room shows every-
where signs of hoarded wealth; a chest full of plate, in which the starved cat hopes
to find something to eat, is in the foreground, together with a heap of bonds and
mortgages; in the background gold is being found, concealed behind the wall-
hangings. On the left of the picture are seen a mother and her daughter, Sarah
Young, whom the Rake has ruined under promise of marriage and now proposes
to buy off.

II. *The Levée.* The Rake, now launched into Society, here appears in his ante-
room, surrounded by professors of the arts considered necessary for a man of
fashion – dancing and fencing, music, prize-fighting, etc. A musician is playing

Fig. 15:
A Rake's Progress
I: The Heir
Photograph:
John Webb

over a Handel opera at the harpsichord. A fencing-master, probably a certain Mr
Dubois, is on his right. Next to him is Figg, the prize-fighter, holding two quarter
staves; then Harris, the dancing master, with behind him Charles Bridgeman, the
landscape gardener, holding a plan. Then follows Rakewell himself, perusing an
introduction from 'W. Stab', presented by 'Captain Hackem'. On the extreme right
are a horn-player (probably a huntsman) and a jockey holding a silver punch-
bowl, indicating Tom's taste in sports.

III. *The Orgy* (Fig.16). The scene is laid at the Rose Tavern, Covent Garden, where
Tom, who is drunk, is spending the early hours of the morning with a party of
prostitutes, after having, apparently, been engaged in fighting the Watch, as he
has captured a horn, lantern and staff as trophies, which lie on the floor by his
chair. One woman is relieving him of his watch, another is spouting wine at a
third, across the table, who is about to retaliate with a knife, whilst, in the
background, another is holding a lighted candle to a map of the world, as though
determined on setting the world on fire. On the left, a tattered girl is singing
ballads, while musicians are adding to the noise. In the foreground a dancer is
undressing, while Leather Coat, well-known porter of the Rose, brings in a salver
for her to posture upon. The name of the tavern is on the rim. Of the portraits of
Roman emperors decorating the wall, only that of Nero is unmutilated.

Fig. 16:
A Rake's Progress
III: The Orgy
Photograph:
John Webb

IV. *The Arrest* (Fig.17). By this time the Rake has run through his first fortune, and is being arrested for debt at the top of St James's Street, while on his way to a *levée* at St James's Palace for the Queen's birthday. Fortune, however, is temporarily kind to him as Sarah Young, formerly deserted by him, is shown coming to his assistance with her slender savings. Amongst the incidental figures is a lamp-lighter who, not paying attention to his own work, is spilling the oil from the street lamps on to the Rake's head. Queen Caroline was born on St David's Day, and consequently a Welsh gentleman and one of the bailiffs are shown wearing leeks in their hats.

V. *The Marriage.* One fortune already wasted, the Rake, to satisfy his craving for dissipation, marries an elderly, one-eyed, but rich lady. The ceremony is taking place in the old and neglected parish church of St Marylebone, faithfully portrayed down to an inscription on the pews (the inscription survived the demolition of the church and its successor and is still preserved at St Marylebone). The parson and clerk are droning the service, while in the background the discarded girl, Sarah Young, who holds a baby in her arms, is endeavouring to enter the church in the forlorn hope of stopping the marriage. An amorous dog and wall-eyed bitch in the foreground make a grotesque analogy with the human ceremony.

VI. *The Gaming House.* Thus possessed of a second fortune, the Rake renews his wild career and in this scene, amongst gamblers and cheats, has again lost everything, and is now cursing his fate. Sitting by the fire on the left, in an apparently listless condition, is a highwayman with a pistol and mask protruding from his pocket; whilst on the right a nobleman is obtaining advances from a money-lender to enable him to continue his play. The scene is set at White's Club, an inner circle of the famous Chocolate House in St James's Street, which had recently burned down – smoke is shown curling up from behind the wall panelling. The Watch are breaking in.

VII. *The Prison.* This scene represents the interior of the Fleet Prison, to which the Rake has been committed for debt. He already shows signs of incipient madness, to which the troubles which he is going through are a contributing cause. Behind him the gaoler is pressing him for the settlement of his weekly 'hotel' bill while a pot-boy is demanding payment for his liquor before handing it over. On the table is his manuscript play, which has just been returned by Rich, the manager of Covent Garden Theatre, with a letter declining it. Sarah Young with her child is shown in a faint, whilst the Rake's enraged wife is engaged in taunting him.

VIII. *The Madhouse,* to which the Rake has been removed to end his days – the last scene. He is surrounded by other victims of insanity; the ever-faithful Sarah Young visits and weeps over him. In the background is a lady, accompanied by her maid,who has come to Bedlam merely in order to see one of the sights of the town. Amongst the insane are inmates who conceive of themselves as a tailor, the Pope, a poet, musician, astronomer, and a king. The man drawing lines on the wall is an allusion to William Whiston's proposed method of discovering the longitude by firing bombs.

AN ELECTION

These four pictures were painted by Hogarth in 1754–55 and are supposed to allude to the Oxfordshire election of 1754. They were engraved, 1755–58, by Hogarth and others. The pictures were bought from the artist by David Garrick for 200 gns and acquired by Sir John Soane at the sale of Mrs Garrick's effects in 1823 for 1,650 gns. Knocking down the lot, the auctioneer observed, 'As returning officer I have the honour of declaring that John Soane, Esq., is the successful candidate in this warmly contested election'. The paintings are as follows:

I. *An Election Entertainment* (Fig.18). The scene is the inn of a country town, in which a 'treat' is being given for the friends of the Whig candidates, both of whom are seen on the left of the picture. The one receiving attention from a fat old woman (while a child fingers his ring and a man behind burns his wig with a pipe) is said to be a portrait of Thomas Potter (1718–59), politician and wit. Behind him the other candidate suffers the maudlin attentions of a tipsy man. Further to the right a guzzling parson has taken off his wig to mop his bald head. Behind him is a group of musicians and above their heads is a slashed portrait of William III (symbol of Whig principles, the inference being perhaps the ignorance or deser-tion of principle by the company present). The woman playing the viol is said to be a portrait of 'Fiddling Nan' who was well known in Oxfordshire. Further again to the right a man is singing 'An Old Woman Clothed in Grey', accompanying the song with traditional puppet-face drawn on the back of his hand. We have Hogarth's authority for identifying the singer as John Parnell (later Sir John, a well-known Dublin attorney), who begged the introduction of his features as a favour. Outside the window, a procession of the opposing Tory party is passing, with an effigy inscribed 'No Jews' (in 1753 the Whigs had passed an act to allow foreign Jews resident in England to become naturalised citizens). Bricks are being hurled in through the window and an election agent has been struck (he is on the right in the foreground). A chamber-pot is being emptied on to the crowd outside and, on the right, men with staves and a sword appear to be preventing a forced entry, whilst a

puritanical tailor is declining a bribe, in spite of the protestations of his wife. The Mayor, at the head of the table, has fainted from a surfeit of oysters and is being bled by a surgeon. In the foreground a man with a broken head, for which he is being treated, internally and externally, with liquor, appears to have captured a banner, inscribed 'Give us our eleven days'. This alludes to the change of the calendar in September 1752, when Britain adopted the Gregorian calendar and had to omit eleven days, passing straight from 3 September to 14 September. The ignorant thought that the omitted days were being eliminated from their lives. Behind this figure a boy mixes punch in a mash-tub, while in the left-hand corner is a Quaker, reading a promissory note for which he seems disinclined to part with the parcel of finery intended as gifts to voters' wives.

II. *Canvassing for Votes.* This scene takes place in front of the Royal Oak, head-quarters of the Court (Tory) party. A young farmer is being bribed by the host to dine there, while the host of the Crown, further down the street, presses a similar bribe. Both bribes are accepted. In front of an open window in the Royal Oak, where two electors are guzzling, a porter has just deposited a bale of gifts before 'Tim^y. Partitool, Esq.', to whom he presents a letter. Partitool, meanwhile, is buying trinkets from a Jewish pedlar for two women – presumably wives or daughters of electors – on the balcony of the inn. At the doorway below, the hostess of the Royal Oak counts the profits of her share in the election proceedings, while a grenadier watches enviously from within, and an old figurehead (representing the British lion devouring the lily of France) serves her as a seat. The inn sign is of particular interest. The sign proper is a painted panel in a carved frame, showing Charles II in the oak, while Roundhead horsemen search for him; but fixed over this is a larger panel of topical application. In the upper half we see the Horse Guards and the Treasury. The architecture of the former is satirized by the substitution of a beer-barrel for the cupola and the decapitation of the royal coachman by the excessive lowness of the centre arch. Gold for election expenses is pouring out of a Treasury window and being loaded into a wagon marked 'Oxford'. In the lower half of the panel, 'Punch, candidate for Guzzletown', is distributing largesse from a wheelbarrow to two men and an old woman. On the right of the picture in the foreground is another inn, the Portobello. Here a garrulous barber is explaining to a cobbler how Admiral Vernon captured Portobello (1739) with six ships only – the ships being repre-sented by pieces of broken clay pipe. At the inn in the background, the Crown, which is also the seat of the Excise authority, a free fight is proceeding, and two men are dragging down the inn sign with a rope. A third, kneeling on the beam over the sign, is sawing through it, oblivious of the fact that when the inn sign, the crown, falls, he falls with it. From a window of the inn a man fires on the mob.

III. *The Polling*. The polling-booth, with a motley assortment of voters coming up to take the oath affirming their right to vote. First, on the right, is an old soldier, who has lost a leg and both hands. He places a wooden peg on the Bible, at which a lawyer protests, while his colleague of the opposing party emphatically scorns the objections. An idiot in a chair follows. The man in fetters, who has carried him up, is identified (in the engraving only, however) as Dr Shebbeare (1709–88), who was imprisoned for abuse of the legislature in his novel, *Marriage* (1754). There follows a man wrapped in a blanket, who is dying, or possibly dead (an allusion, perhaps, to an anecdote of a corpse who was made to emit a 'vote' at an election). A blind beggar and cripple follow. Two of the candidates are seen at the back of the booth, one anxiously mopping his brow as he scans the state of the poll. The other, seen in profile, is being sketched by an artist, to the amusement of two onlookers. A woman on the outer edge of the crowd is selling a libellous ballad, headed by a figure on the gallows. On the left, in the middle-distance, is a coach, the purport of which is allegorical. The Union Jack, blazoned on the door, proclaims it the coach of Britannia, who is looking out of the window in alarm. On the box, the coachman and footman are gambling (one cheating the other), while the horses plunge towards the river and the coach collapses on its broken

Fig. 19:
An Election
IV: Chairing
the Member
Photograph:
John Webb

springs. In the background a stone bridge is jammed with traffic leaving the election scene, while beyond is a landscape with a hill-top village church.

IV. *Chairing the Member* (Fig.19). The triumphal procession of the 'old interest', the Tory party, whose banner and blue favours are seen among the crowd. Of the two candidates, one only is seen in the picture, but the presence of the second is suggested by his shadow on the side of the wall of the building in the background. Seated in an old-fashioned chair, carried shoulder-high by his supporters, the successful Member is said to bear more than accidental resemblance to George Bubb Dodington (1691–1762), later Baron Melcombe. Above the Member's head flies a goose, perhaps in ironic imitation of the eagle which hovers over Alexander in Le Brun's painting of the *Battle of Arbela*. The sow and her litter, loose among the mob and making for the stream, are, perhaps, intended to suggest an analogy with the Gadarene swine, as well as with the swinish behaviour of the man sticking his head in an empty beer-barrel. The sow has knocked over an old woman, who disappears behind the prominent central figure of a man wielding a flail. This weapon has struck one of the bearers, though it was aimed at the one-legged sailor below, who appears to be the owner of the performing bear on the right. The bear, while his master's attention is diverted, is nosing into the panniers of a man on a donkey, who is giving him a beating, while the donkey leisurely eats a thistle. On the bear's back rides a monkey with a carbine over his shoulder. The carbine points at one of two little chimney-sweeps, on the churchyard wall, who is placing a pair of gingerbread spectacles on a skull, while the other contrives to drench the monkey from a source prudently concealed by the capping of the gate pier. Nearby a young woman, fainting at the sight of the fighting, is being supported by two attendants. On the church tower, to the right, a sundial, dated 1755, bears the inscription *pulvis et umbra sumus*. The house on the left, into which dishes are being carried by three servants with red favours, is evidently the rendezvous of the defeated party, who are regaling themselves while they watch the discomfiture of the elected Member. Nichols records a tradition that 'the old Duke of Newcastle appears at the window'; this can, however, only be the figure wearing the Garter ribbon, whose features are not visible. The significance of the window above where a hand is seen writing at a desk is not clear, though it may allude to the penurious conditions of a political pamphleteer. The figure of a half-naked sailor, wearing a red favour and taking a plug of tobacco from a paper marked 'Kirton's Best' (an allusion to a London tobacconist who ruined his constitution and his fortune by being busy in the Oxfordshire election) suggests that he is enjoying a reward for his services. His broken cutlass lies behind him on the stream's bank.

Apart from the two series of Hogarth paintings already described, the following pictures are displayed in this room. Those *visible with all the movable planes closed* are described first, working clockwise round the room starting from the west side around the doorway. The pictures hidden within the cabinets are then listed, working round in the same order. Pictures are listed in order working from the top downwards on each wall or plane.

West Side

Over the doorway. William Beechey, Portrait of Soane's friend Sir Francis Bourgeois, RA (exhib. RA 1813); Richard Westall, 'Milton composing Paradise Lost' (watercolour; exhib. RA 1802).

Left of doorway. Charles Lock Eastlake, 'Una delivering the Red Cross Knight from the Cave of Despair' (exhib. RA 1830); John Jackson, Portrait of Sir John Soane in Masonic costume as Grand Superintendent of Works (commissioned by Soane in 1828; exhib. RA 1830); Henry Fuseli, 'The Italian Count, or Ezzelier, Count of Ravenna musing over the body of Meduna, slain by him for infidelity during his absence in the Holy Land' (exhib. RA 1780) Fig.14, p.22.

Right of doorway. William Hamilton, 'The Landing of Richard II at Milford Haven'; John Jackson, posthumous portrait of Mrs Soane with her dog, Fanny, executed in 1831 after drawings by Flaxman (Fig.48, p.76) and Ward (p.72) and a miniature by William Dance (p.68); Edward Bird, 'The Cheat Detected' (exhib. RA 1814).

North Side

F Zuccarelli, landscape with figures; Sir Augustus Wall Callcott, 'The Thames below Greenwich' (commissioned by Soane; exhib. RA 1822); Francis Bourgeois, 'A Hen defending her chickens from the cat'; Maria Cosway, 'Persian lady worshipping the rising sun'.

East Side (above the fireplace)

Fragment of a cartoon (i.e. design) for a tapestry, 'The Presentation in the Temple', attributed by Soane to Raphael but probably by Tommaso Vincidor, one of his assistants; Sir James Thornhill, design for ceiling of the Queen's State Bedchamber at Hampton Court Palace; John Flaxman, copy of a fragment of a 'Raphael' cartoon (the original is in the National Gallery of Scotland) of the Massacre of the Innocents.

South Side

William Hodges, 'A view of the Mosque at Fatehpur Sikri, near Agra, India' (exhib. RA 1794) and 'A view near Agra, India' (in fact a view of the garden side of the mosque at Chunar).

We now turn to the pictures *inside the cabinets* and behind the movable planes, again working clockwise. On each plane the descriptions begin at the top and work down.

West Side

Left-hand cabinet, left of the doorway

Inside the movable plane. Design by Soane for an entrance to Bagshot Park (exhib. RA 1799); mezzotint of 'The Prosperity of Great Britain contrasted with the Misery of France', a propaganda subject of 1794; two landscapes with ruins by Antonio Zucchi.

In the recess. Design by Soane for the north front of the Bank of England, as originally intended (exhib. RA 1810); Joseph Michael Gandy, 'Architectural Ruins – a Vision', watercolour showing the Rotunda and Dividend Warrant Office at the Bank of England as if they were Roman ruins (exhib. RA, 1832); drawing of a dog, French 18th-century (formerly attributed to Rubens); two watercolour sketches by John Webber of scenes from Sterne's 'Sentimental Journey'; an oil painting of a landcape by Cornelis Decker (Haarlem, *c.*1650).

Right-hand cabinet

Inside the movable plane. Three architectural compositions for stage-settings by members of the Bibiena family (ink and wash, now much faded); view by George Barret senior, taken 'in Mr Lock's park at Leatherhead', executed in watercolour.

In the recess. Four engravings by Giovanni Battista Piranesi from his *Vedute di Roma* (presented to Soane in Rome by the artist).

North Side

Inside left plane. Soane's project for an entrance from Piccadilly to Green Park, designed in 1796 (exhib. RA 1826); drawing by J M Gandy showing 'The Temple of Ceres at Eleusis' (exhib. RA 1815); a small watercolour by J M W Turner, 'The Refectory at Kirkstall Abbey' (exhib. RA 1798; see also p.98); two ink sketches of landscapes by Jacob van Ruisdael.

Inside right plane. Scenes by Charles-Louis Clérisseau of Classical ruins.

In the recess. Fifteen ink and wash drawings by Giovanni Battista Piranesi of the temples at Paestum in southern Italy. These original drawings were subsequently engraved (total of twenty plates) and published by Piranesi's son Francesco in 1778 as '*Differentes Vues de quelques restes de trois grands edifices qui subsistent encores dans le milieu de l'ancienne ville de Pesto*'.

South Side

Inside first left-hand plane. Designs by Soane. J M Gandy, views of the exterior and interior of the National Debt Redemption and Life Annuities Office in the Old Jewry, erected 1818; J M Gandy, interior of the new 3% Reduced Annuities Office at the Bank during construction, 1818; J M Gandy 'Architectural Visions of early fancy in the gay morning of youth and dreams in the evening of life' (exhib. RA 1820). This last, which is a composition of designs that were never executed, includes the Triumphal Bridge (left) for which Soane was awarded the Royal Academy Gold Medal in 1776 and of which he exhibited later variations in 1799 and 1806. Also shown are student designs done on his tour to Italy (1778–80) and the House of Lords design of 1794–96 (right). This last and the entrance to the London Parks (foreground) were among the disappointments of Soane's later life. In the background (top left) Admiral Lord Nelson's funeral procession (which took place in 1805) is wending its way through the buildings. Soane's ticket to the funeral survives in the Museum's archives.

Inside first right-hand plane. Designs by Soane. J M Gandy, design for buildings at the corner of Downing Street, including a triumphal arch, (exhib. RA 1826; compare with the model on the Dining Room mantelshelf see p.5); J M Gandy, view of the New Masonic Hall, adjoining Freemasons' Hall, Great Queen Street, by day (exhib. RA 1829; now replaced by a new building on the same site, a few hundred yards west of the Museum in Great Queen Street; a lamp-lit night view of the same interior hangs in the North Drawing Room see p. 82); J M Gandy, first design for the State Paper Office with a section and a plan of the ground floor (exhib. RA 1831).

Outside second left-hand plane. Designs by Soane. J M Gandy, Bird's-eye view of design for a royal palace, made from studies in Rome in 1779 (exhib. RA 1828; the intended site was Hyde Park); J M Gandy, design for an entrance into London (exhib. RA 1826); J M Gandy, sundry views of various offices etc. in the Bank of England (exhib. RA 1822).

Outside second, right-hand plane. Designs by Soane. J M Gandy, designs for uniform entrances for Hyde Park, St James's Park and the Western entrance to London (1829); J M Gandy, views of John Soane's house at 13 Lincoln's Inn Fields in 1822 (exhib. RA 1822; this is amongst the best evidence we have for the early appearance of rooms in this building). J M Gandy, 'Public and Private Buildings Executed by Sir John Soane between 1780 and 1815' (exhib. RA 1818). This composition shows over one hundred of Soane's buildings, depicted either as models or paintings, set within a Soanean interior and dominated by the Bank of England (top centre), with the Dulwich Picture Gallery to its right. In shadow, on the left, is the façade of this Museum. Beside it, draped funereally in black, is the tomb Soane designed for his wife. The space is lit by an oil lamp behind a reflector bearing Soane's coat of arms. In the foreground, right, Soane is seated at his desk.

Inside second left-hand plane. Designs by Soane. J M Gandy, design for the approach to a Triumphal Bridge, designed in 1776 (exhib. RA 1799); J M Gandy, bird's-eye view of the Triumphal Bridge, designed in 1776 and here drawn in 1821, shown spanning the Thames on the site of the present Lambeth Bridge. (Soane never lost his enthusiasm for the Triumphal Bridge design that had earned him the Gold Medal of the Royal Academy and membership of the Academy at Parma and helped him to win the visit to Italy that was to have such important consequences for his career. There are several variants of this design among his drawings including one with the order changed to Greek Doric); J M Gandy, bird's-eye view of a design for a royal residence on Constitution Hill (in Green Park; exhib. RA 1821, see also pp. 80 & 82). (On the accession of George IV in 1820, Soane had hoped to be invited to build a new royal palace. He was the official architect for Crown properties in the Westminster area and could have expected to be given the commission which, however, went instead to John Nash, who remodelled old Buckingham House, subsequently re-named Buckingham Palace).

Inside second right-hand plane. Designs by Soane. J M Gandy, the Library at Pitzhanger Manor, Ealing (exhib. RA 1803; the house was Soane's country villa, built in 1800. It has been restored and is open to the public see p. 148); J M Gandy, the Breakfast Room at Pitzhanger Manor, 1802; J M Gandy, buildings erected or designed by Sir John Soane shown as an exhibition of models and drawings in an expanded and fantastical version of the Picture Room (drawn c.1824).

THE PICTURE ROOM RECESS

With the second planes open, '*a view is presented of the upper part of the Monk's Room, and the recess therein, in the back of which is a large window, glazed with painted glass*'. In front of the window is a plaster statue of a Nymph by Richard Westmacott, placed here on the completion of the Picture Room in 1824. It was probably the preparatory model for the marble version (exhib. RA 1828) at Castle Howard which was destroyed in the fire of November 1940. At the foot of the statue is a model of the Threadneedle Street front of the Bank of England. Behind the Nymph is a large model of the Board of Trade.

In this space are displayed:

Left-hand end wall. Soane's design for a mausoleum for the Earl of Chatham (exhib. RA 1799); Clérisseau, view of a sepulchral chamber (see Fig.60 p.128); Francis Bourgeois, 'Mr Kemble as Coriolanus, Act IV, Scene I' (exhib. RA 1797). On the shelf below is a Javanese bronze pavilion with figures, probably late 18th- or early 19th-century.

Right-hand end wall. Lallemand, View of the Pyramid of Caius Cestius, Rome; Clérisseau, Antique ruins; Antoine Watteau, 'Les Noces' or 'L'Accordée du Village'

Fig. 20:
The Picture Room Recess
Photograph: Martin Charles

Fig. 21: 'St Hugues denouncing vengeance on the the shepherd of Cormayer in the valley of d'Aoust' by J M W Turner, watercolour, 1803 *Photograph: Geremy Butler*

(purchased by Soane in 1802). On the shelf below are various items including a fine Roman bronze lamp and a Roman tripod stand, perhaps from Pompeii or Herculaneum, along with two South Italian vases of the 4th century BC.

Round the window-opening; from left to right. Clérisseau drawings of antique ruins; portrait of Dr Messenger Monsey, physician to the Royal Hospital at Chelsea; design by Soane for the Tivoli corner at the Bank of England; design by Soane for two corridors at the Bank and the entrance hall at McCartney House, Blackheath; design by Soane for a new House of Lords, 1794 (probably one of the drawings exhib. RA 1800); J M W Turner 'St Hugues denouncing vengeance on the shepherd of Cormayer [sic] in the valley of d'Aoust' (exhib. RA 1803) (Fig.21, and see p.98); Soane's design for the north-west angle (Tivoli Corner) of the Bank of England drawn by J M Gandy (exhib. RA 1824).

In the window recess, left wall; Engraving of a transparency exhibited at the Bank of England as part of the illuminations on the recovery of George III in 1789; J M Gandy, views of the interiors of the Museum, 1822; the south-east angle of the Bank of England. *Right wall.* Bird's-eye view of a design for a Royal Palace; north-east angle of the Bank of England (exhib. RA 1824). *To the left of the window;* Clérisseau, antique ruins; Panini, architectural ruins; Richard Cosway, 'Mars reposing in the lap of Venus'. *To the right of the window.* Clérisseau, antique ruins; Panini, architectural ruins; Richard Cosway, 'Andromache and Astyanax'.

Fig. 22: Terracotta figure of Charles II
by Arnold Quellin, 1685
Photograph: Ole Woldbye

THE BASEMENT STOREY AND CRYPT

As you descend the stairs, above the door on to Whetstone Park (originally
Soane's office door) are the Royal Arms which hung formerly in the Court of
King's Bench, rebuilt by Soane in 1820–24. They are made of some form of papier-
mâché and have been cleaned (1991) to reveal the original colours, hidden under
layers of varnish. To the left, facing down the stairs, is a plaster statue of the
Hercules Hesperides which formerly belonged to the sculptor John Flaxman. Also
notice near the foot of the stairs, a mask, taken during her life, of Mrs Sarah
Siddons, the actress.

THE MONK'S PARLOUR AND MONK'S YARD

Descending the stairs we find ourselves in a corridor, to the left of which is the
Monk's Parlour, formed in 1824 at the same time as the Picture Room above it.
Glancing immediately left at the bottom of the stairs there is a view into the
Monk's Parlour through the only door in the house to retain its original coloured
glass. To the right lies the older part of the 'Crypt', built in 1808–12 but substan-
tially altered by James Wild in the late 19th century. On the wall beyond is a large
cast of one of the roundels designed by Soane's friend, the sculptor Thomas

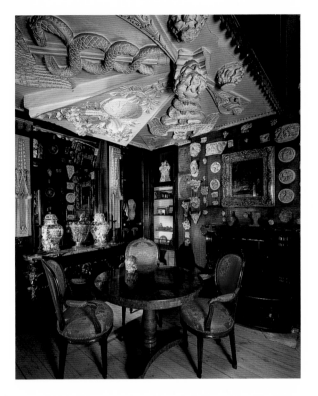

Fig. 23:
The Monk's Parlour
Photograph:
Martin Charles

Banks, after the Roman reliefs of Sol and Luna ('Sun' and 'Moon' or 'Morning' and 'Evening') on the Arch of Constantine. Soane used Banks' roundels on his Lothbury Arch at the Bank of England.

The Monk's Parlour or, as Soane called it, the *'Parloir of Padre Giovanni'* is part of the 'monastic' suite which Soane installed in this part of the Museum, and which consists of the Monk's Cell or Oratory, the Parlour itself and the Monk's Yard, with the ruined cloister and tomb, visible through the Parlour window. Soane's intention here seems to have been to to satirize the rising fashion for Gothic antiquarianism while at the same time producing a picturesque arrangement of space and objects. After Mrs Soane's death in 1815 Soane began to refer to his 'Monk's Cell' at Lincoln's Inn Fields in his Notebook (his diary). At this date he was probably referring to the Study (p.10). He also, in the summer of 1816, visited the Hermit's Cell and castle ruins at Knaresborough. The walls of the Hermit's Cell there were adorned with Gothic ornaments and this almost certainly influenced Soane when he was devising the Monk's Parlour.

Fig. 24: The Monk's Yard looking east,
22 August 1825, watercolour by J M Gandy
Photograph: Geremy Butler

The form of the Monk's Parlour and its relationship to the Picture Room and Recess above, is highly original. The front (south) portion of the Parlour ascending into the space between the recess and the folding planes of the Picture Room, has a skylight fitted with yellow-tinted glass. The Parlour contains a medley of objects, most, though by no means all, of a medieval character and intended to produce an atmosphere of studious gloom and to 'impress the spectator with reverence for the monk'. Through the window to the south the Monk's Yard, with its sham ruins, is visible. Soane's description is as follows: 'The Ruins of a Monastery arrest the attention. The interest created in the mind of the spectator, on visiting the abode of the monk, will not be weakened by wandering among the ruins of his once noble monastery. The rich Canopy and other decorations of this venerable spot are objects which cannot fail to produce the most powerful sensations in the minds of the admirers of the piety of our forefathers, who raised such structures for the worship of the Almighty Disposer of events.

'The Tomb of the monk adds to the gloomy scenery of this hallowed place, wherein attention has been given to every minute circumstance. The Pavement, composed of the tops and bottoms of broken bottles, and pebbles found amongst the gravel dug out for the foundation of the monastery, and disposed in symmetry of design, furnishes an admirable lesson of simplicity and economy, and shows the unremitting assiduity of the pious monk. The stone structure, at the head of the monk's grave, contains the remains of Fanny, the faithful companion, the delight, the solace of his leisure hours.

Alas, poor Fanny!

'Amongst these ruins is placed the furnace that heats the water by which the Museum and part of the basement storey of the House is warmed, by means of an ingenious apparatus, the contrivance of Mr A. M. Perkins.

'It may, perhaps, be asked, before leaving this part of the Museum at what period the Monk existed whose masonry is here preserved, and whether he is to be identified with any of those whose deeds have enshrined their names. The answer to these questions is furnished by Horace: Dulce est desipere in loco.'

The quotation ('it is pleasant to be nonsensical in due place') is a warning not to take the 'Parlour of Padre Giovanni' and its attributes too seriously. 'Padre Giovanni' ('Father John') is, of course, an eponym of Sir John Soane himself. The allusion to Fanny is to Mrs Soane's pet dog, seen on her lap in Jackson's portrait (p.30) and in paintings by Ward and Van Assen in the Breakfast Parlour (p.72). Fanny died in 1820 and was first buried in a tomb in the front courtyard of No. 13 before her remains were moved to the Monk's Yard.

One of Soane's preparatory sketches for the north side of the Monk's Parlour shows the side-table in William Kent's late style of about 1745 (in the centre), so it is evident that he regarded this piece as of importance in his scheme. The table is painted black as is the table in the window-bay opposite (this is in Kent's earlier style of about 1730) but neither would have been this colour originally. Black furniture was considered especially appropriate for 'monastic' settings' such as this room, so one must presume that Soane had them painted black. Both tables came from Lord Yarborough's house at Chelsea (see pp.54, and 64). On the table opposite the window stands a lustreware vase from Spain (Manises, near Valencia) of *c.*1700 flanked by a pair of Staffordshire vases, *c.*1800–10. To the left, on a pedestal, is a 16th-century German stoneware jug decorated in relief with a frieze depicting 'Susannah and the Elders'. To the right, also on a pedestal, are two Roman vessels in Verulamium ware, dating from the 1st or 2nd century AD. Behind the vases, through a hinged casement, is the Monk's Cell in which a 15th-century Flemish carved wood crucifixion can be seen.

The chimney-piece is vaguely Gothic in style. Over it hangs a painting on copper, a copy or version of the altar-piece by Fra Bartolommeo in Besançon Cathedral. In the glazed cupboards to either side, originally bookcases, are small objects including a late 17th-century Russo-Greek triptych, an early 16th-century chrismatory, and a collection (one of the earliest) of Peruvian pottery of the pre-Columbian period. When Soane purchased these pots in 1834 he wrote 'I doubt their antiquity but they are uncommon'.

Fig. 25: The Monk's Parlour
Photograph: Martin Charles

On the walls above, and all round the room, are casts, mostly of ornaments in the Gothic style. Some were taken for Soane from Henry VII's chapel at Westminster Abbey, others seem to be early neo-Gothic and therefore of Soane's own time and possibly models for details on his buildings in the Gothic taste. High up, opposite the window and directly beneath the opening planes of the Picture Room, is a fine design model for the Bartholomew Lane façade of the Bank of England, 1825. On the shelf below is a small group of bronzes – 'Angerona', a warrior, 'Flora' and Mars – all 16th- or 17th-century.

The large window contains an elaborate composition of ancient stained glass (mainly Flemish 16th- and 17th-century) within coloured glass borders. Outside may be seen the Monk's Yard with its 'Cloister' consisting of two arches which originally formed window openings in the old House of Lords, Westminster, a 13th-century building demolished in 1822 when Soane built his Royal Gallery. In the centre, between the arches, is a well-preserved late 14th-century canopy removed from the north front of Westminster Hall during the restoration of 1819–20. The arches are surmounted by an 18th-century Corinthian capital on which is a bust of the Duke of York, brother of George IV. Other fragments in the courtyard include several from St Stephen's Chapel, Westminster (14th-century), the old House of Commons. These were removed about 1800, when the building was enlarged to provide accommodation for the Irish members. Soane acquired these fragments while serving as architect to the Office of Works with responsibility for the Government buildings at Westminster.

On the left wall of the window bay is a square patera of oak from the 13th-century ceiling of the Painted Chamber at Westminster. On a bracket above is a small plaster figure of Van Dyck after a sculpture by Rysbrack, purchased at the Richard Cosway sale in 1821. Facing it, on another bracket, is the terracotta model by G B Guelfi for the monument to James Craggs (d.1721) in Westminster Abbey, also purchased at the Cosway sale. The original face has been sliced off and the wooden replacement probably dates from Soane's time. On the table is a small-scale version in plaster of the celebrated Roman statue of the Apollo Belvedere, probably by Flaxman, and flanking the table are two Dutch chairs of c.1700–10 which originally had caned seats. These are now upholstered (1999) in 'crimson flowered silk', as at the time of Soane's death, along with the four armchairs around the circular table. On a bracket high up, on the left of the doorway, is a terracotta figure of Charles II by Arnold Quellin, 1685, probably the model for the statue on the old Royal Exchange, purchased at the Cosway sale in 1821 (Fig.22, p.36). A 17th-century German cross-bow hangs behind the door.

On top of the plan chest, on the west side of the room, is a wooden model of a lantern in an elegant Regency Gothic idiom. This was designed by J W Hiort and

Fig 26: 'The Adoration of the Magi', bas-relief by John Flaxman, RA *Photograph: Geremy Butler*

erected on the roof of Westminster Hall during its restoration in 1819–20. On either side of it are panels of stained glass with scriptural subjects. The glass is German, two panels coming from a church in Cologne and bearing the dates 1692 and 1695. Soane noted *'The Scriptural subjects, represented on glass are suited to the destination of the place, and increase its sombre character'.*

In front of the lantern model is an 18th-century Italian carved wooden figure of a monk with rosary, described by Soane as a portrait of the Parlour's occupant.

THE BASEMENT SOUTH CORRIDOR

Leaving the Monk's Parlour and proceeding straight ahead (westward; mind the step down) *'you enter a Corridor of considerable length ... in the south wall of which* [left] *are three perforations. At the back of these perforations, in a recess, is a plaster Cast of a Chimney-piece, placed, in the reign of Queen Elizabeth, in one of the rooms of the ancient palace at Westminster . . . In the opening of the chimney-piece is a plaster Cast of a design . . . representing Piety'*, a model by John Flaxman for the monument to Mrs Helen Knight (d.1801) at Wolverley Church, Worcestershire. Hanging either side of the chimney-piece cast are two corbels, casts *'from the ruins of Ramsey Abbey'.* In the opening between the two arches is one of an original pair of what Soane called *'antique Heraldic Monsters'*, in fact a plaster Japanese lion-dog.

Opposite the Recess, within the arch are a pair of standing figures of 'Faith' and 'Charity', models by Flaxman for the monument to Lady Spencer at Great Brington, Northants, c.1818. Leaning against the wall of the arch is a relief of a weeping cherub – a model for the Soane tomb in St Pancras Gardens (see p.148).

Within the arch, hanging on the walls, are four small bas reliefs by John Flaxman. Left: 'Satan flying from the angels Gabriel and Ithuriel' (top) and 'Adam and Eve in Paradise', both subjects from John Milton's 'Paradise Lost'. Right: 'The Adoration of the Magi' (top; Fig.26) and 'Joseph's Dream'. The two Gothic cast-iron chairs were probably manufactured c.1800–15 at the Carron Iron Works in Scotland.

THE BASEMENT ANTE-ROOM

Continue westwards along the Corridor to enter the basement Ante-Room which opens up to the left and has double doors offering a view into the Monument Court. From here you can view the lower part of the *'Architectural pasticcio, about thirty feet high'*, a column of architectural fragments in the centre of the courtyard. Its base is a cylindrical antique altar, which was the base for the cast of the Apollo Belvedere in the Dome area when it belonged to Lord Burlington at

Fig 27: View of the pasticcio *in*
the Monument Court
Photograph: Lyall Thow

Chiswick (see p. 60). On top of the altar is what Soane described as '*a marble Capital of Hindu Architecture*', now known to be a Moroccan capital of the Saadian period (1554–1664), identical to those used in the complex of royal tombs in Marrakesh. The altar and the capital were both part of Soane's original *pasticcio*, preserved when it was taken down in 1896. All the other parts of the column, except the topmost element and the cast iron urns, were re-carved by Fairhaven of Anglesey Abbey for the re-creation of the column in April 2004. These include the magnificent capital based on those of the Roman Temple of Vesta at Tivoli (as used by Soane at the Bank of England) which rests on the Moroccan capital.

In the centre of the Ante-Room are two tables. One is in fact a box for drawings, screwed to a frame with legs. Here Soane kept drawings for Bank of England Branch Banks. The other table is eighteenth-century with a fine grey marble top, full of fossils. On this are two rows of busts. Back row, from left to right: Roman marble bust, possibly of the Emperor Augustus; plaster bust by John Gibson of the actor John Philip Kemble; neo-classical (18th-century) marble bust of a youth in the Early Imperial Roman style (we do not know whether this is a portrait of a man in a Roman style or an imitation of an ancient head). Front row, from left to right: plaster bust, a copy of the head of one of the sons of Laocoön in the famous Antique statue now in the Vatican Museum (a small version of the Laocoön, made by John Flaxman, is in the Museum South Passage, see p.56); plaster bust by Louis Parfait Merlieux of Baron Cuvier. (The Frenchman Georges Cuvier was an anatomist, educational reformer and adviser to Napoleon on scientific matters. This bust formerly belonged to Sir Thomas Lawrence to whom it had been presented by Madame Cuvier). Plaster bust, a copy of the head of one of the sons of Laocoön (a pair with the other). In the west (fireplace) wall are two recesses. In the left-hand recess is a cast after the antique of 'Cupid and Psyche'. In the right-hand recess is a bust of Sir William Chambers, the architect, one of the first works of Richard Westmacott. It was exhibited in the Royal Academy in 1797, when Westmacott was 22 and had just returned from Rome. On the base is inscribed in gold an extract from a letter to Soane from J W Hiort, of the Office of Works, from which it appears that the bust was commissioned by the officers of the Department, of which Chambers, as Surveyor-General, had been the head, and was handed over to Soane, for his Museum, in 1832, when the Office was merged with the Office of Woods and Forests. Above the fireplace is a plaster spandrel in the form of an eagle from the staircase of the Prince Regent's London Palace, Carlton House (built by Henry Holland from 1783 and demolished in 1827; see p.65). To its right is what is thought to be a life mask of the sculptor Thomas Banks, a close friend of Soane, which was acquired by Soane from the collection of another friend, the sculptor John Flaxman.

On the South wall (to the left of the door) is a cast of a Roman relief of *Endymion* in the Capitoline Museum, Rome. Above it hangs a relief of 'Angels Releasing a Captive' (thought to be St Peter) by Thomas Banks. The full-scale sculpture for which this was the model is part of the memorial to the Hon. Mary Pakenham at Laracor in Ireland (1791). Over the door is a portrait medallion of G F Handel, the composer, possibly by Roubiliac.

To the left of the window is a cast of 'The Apotheosis of Homer' from an original Roman marble (see p.12).

The crude chair provided for the attendant is one of four which were part of Soane's kitchen furniture.

When the green door is open, the visitor may go through to reach the bottom of the main staircase where the public lavatories may be found. At other times the stairs by the Monk's Parlour should be used to return to the Ground Floor.

Returning to the South Corridor and continuing westward we find on our right a series of arches, the walls of which are hung with antique fragments and plaster casts. The principal exhibits are as follows:

First arch: Cast of a Hellenistic Roman relief of *Perseus and Andromeda* from the Capitoline Museum, Rome. Like the *Endymion*, this previously belonged to John Flaxman.

On the left jamb of the arch: three torsos. The two top and bottom are Roman copies from Hellenistic originals while the centre one (M1034) is a good Graeco-Roman specimen of an Apoxyomenos (an athlete scraping himself with a strigil after vigorous exercise).

On the right jamb: torso (? a figure representing one of the Seasons) from the lid of a Niobid sarcophagus; torso of Dionysius, Roman copy of a 4th-century original. On the face of the pier, to the left, is a fragment (a centaur) from a Roman sarcophagus (M1486).

Third arch: (on a stand) Sir Francis Chantrey: a sleeping child. The original marble (*c.*1820) was executed for Sir Thomas Dyke Acland, and was at the family seat at Killerton, Devon, until 1943. On the face of the pier to the left of this arch are two Roman fragments: a male torso in black marble (M1051) and part of a frieze, probably from the Domus Augustiana in Rome (M636).

THE CATACOMBS

This space opens up on the left and bears this name because it is lined with tiers of box-like recesses containing cinerary urns.

The cinerary urns are Roman, 1st or 2nd century AD, and would have been used to contain the ashes of the dead in a Roman catacomb or 'columbarium'. They include a number which once belonged to G B Piranesi in Rome. On the south wall, above the niches, is 'Hercules holding Cerberus' by Henry Webber, a plaster version of a celebrated French marble, Augustin Pajou's 'Pluto keeping Cerberus in Chains' (in the Louvre, Paris) which he submited as his 'morceau de réception' to the Académie Royale in 1760. The plaster is coloured to imitate bronze. Below are two panels, carved in relief on both front and back with theatrical masks and other motifs (similar panels have been found at Pompeii, where they served as ventilation openings).

THE WEST CORRIDOR

Continuing past the catacombs, through the door may be seen the New Court, so called because it was taken into the Museum in 1889–90, when the New Picture Room (on the ground floor; p.62) and ground floor Ante-Room (p.65) were built. In the court is a lead cistern bearing initials and a date, E P 1764. This was in the kitchen of the previous house on the No. 12 site and was made for Edmund Proudfoot who owned the house from 1763 to 1767. To the right of the door hangs a Roman terracotta cresting plaque (decorative feature for the ridge of a roof) from the Emperor Hadrian's Villa at Tivoli, *once in the possession of Dr. Chauncey*. Opposite this, in a recess, is a cast of a crouching Venus (the original is in the Vatican Museums) formerly in the collection of the painter, George Romney.

On the tall plaster column, painted in imitation of porphyry is a colossal bronze head of Jupiter (Italian; 18th-century), presented to Soane by the Hon. Mr. Melville.

At the North end of the Corridor are two obelisks which formerly served as lamp posts in Lincoln's Inn Fields. Between them is a bust believed by Soane to be a portrait of John James Heidegger, *'master of the revels to King George II, and remarkable for being the first who introduced masquerades into this country'*; but this identification is doubtful.

Hanging either side of the arched opening to the sepulchral chamber are Egyptian limestone stelae of the XXII Dynasty (*c.*900 BC).

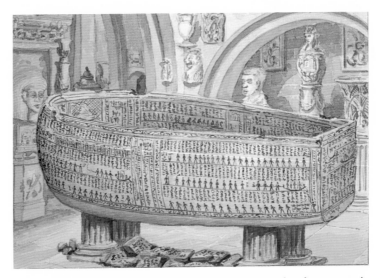

Fig. 29: The sarcophagus of Seti I as depicted in a preparatory watercolour for an engraved
plate in Soane's 1830 *Description* of his residence *Photograph: Geremy Butler*

THE SEPULCHRAL CHAMBER

Now moving eastwards we see how the Crypt opens into the upper part of the
Museum and is lit from the skylight of the 'Dome' above. All this portion was
built in 1808–09, while Soane was still living in No. 12, and is thus the earliest of
the buildings now comprising the Museum.

'*Under the arch leading into the Sepulchral Chamber are two large antique vases*',
raised on columns. One is a clay amphora of the Roman Imperial period the
other is an alabaster cinerary urn raised on a column. Roman cinerary urns made
of alabaster are extremely rare and would only have been used for the ashes
of persons of high rank in the Empire. This is inscribed C. VARI, C.F. POMIVLI. /
PROCVII. P.R. Soane purchased it for £1 5s at Lord Mendip's sale, 1802.

In the centre of the Sepulchral Chamber stands the Sarcophagus of the
Egyptian King Seti I (reigned from 1294 BC until his death in 1279 BC), one of the
principal treasures of the Museum. It was discovered in October 1817 by Giovanni
Battista Belzoni who was excavating the tomb under the patronage of Henry Salt
and other Englishmen interested in the exploration of the great Necropolis of
Thebes. Belzoni brought the sarcophagus to England and it was deposited in the
British Museum in September 1821. In April 1824 it was offered to the Trustees of
that museum for £2,000, but they declined to purchase it. Soane had already

obtained the reversion of the offer and the sarcophagus was brought here on 12 May 1824.

In March of the following year, Soane held three separate evening receptions in honour of its acquisition and to help Mrs Belzoni, the discoverer's widow, whose Exhibition in Leicester Square (featuring a reconstruction of Seti I's tomb) was to open the following week. He invited his guests to 'view the sarcophagus by lamplight' and employed William Collins, manfacturer of stained glass and dealer in lighting appliances, to provide lamps throughout the house and inside the sarcophagus. Benjamin Robert Haydon described one of the evenings in a letter to Mary Russell Mitford: 'The first person I met . . . was Coleridge . . . [then] I was pushed up against Turner, the landscape painter with his red face and white waistcoat, and . . . was carried off my legs, and irretrievably bustled to where the sarcophagus lay . . . It was the finest fun imaginable to see the people come into the Library after wandering about below, amidst tombs and capitals, and

Fig 30:
The Sepulchral Chamber and the Dome
Area above, watercolour
by J M Gandy, 8 September 1825
Photograph: Geremy Butler

shafts, and noseless heads, with a sort of expression of delighted relief at finding themselves among the living, and with coffee and cake. Fancy delicate ladies of fashion dipping their pretty heads into an old mouldy, fusty hierogliphicked coffin, blessing their stars at its age, wondering whom it contained . . . . Just as I was beginning to meditate, the Duke of Sussex, with a star on his breast, and an asthma inside it, came squeezing and wheezing along the narrow passage, driving all the women before him like a Blue-Beard, and putting his royal head into the coffin, added his wonder to the wonder of the rest.'

In Soane's time little was known of Egyptian art and his own description of the sarcophagus is as follows:

'*This marvellous effort of human industry and perseverance is supposed to be at least three thousand years old . . . and is considered of pre-eminent interest, not only as a work of human skill and labour, but as illustrative of the custom, arts, religion and government of a very ancient and learned people. The surface . . . is covered externally and internally with hieroglyphics, comprehending a written language, which it is to be hoped the labours of modern literati will render intelligible.*'

It remained for Sir E A Wallis Budge to describe and interpret the sarcophagus completely in 1908. The following note is by the same authority:

'The *sarcophagus* of Seti I is formed of a well-chosen monolithic block of limestone, or aragonite, which was hewn from the famous quarry near the town called by the Greeks "Alabastronpolis"; the stone is white, close in texture, and hard, and comparatively thick slices of it are semi-transparent. It is 9ft 4in. long, 3ft 8in. wide near the shoulders, 1ft 10in. wide at the head, 2ft wide at the foot, and its height varies from 2ft 8in. at the shoulders to 2ft 3in. at the foot. In thickness the stone varies from 2.5in. to 4in.

'The *Cover* likewise was formed of a monolithic block of limestone, and was about 1ft 3in. high; it was broken probably between 900 and 800 BC, when it was found necessary to remove the body of the king to a place of safety in the hiding place at Dêr al-Bahari, where the mummy was found in 1881. Seventeen fragments were found by Belzoni in the sarcophagus chamber in 1817, and two or three others were discovered in one of the corridors of the tomb some eighty years later . . . . The cover was held in its place on the sarcophagus by means of a projecting ridge, which ran all round and fitted into a rectangular cavity on the inner side of the upper edge of the sarcophagus. The cover was probably swung over the sarcophagus by means of ropes which passed through holes, of which three are still visible, and lowered into its place, care being taken to protect the brittle edges of both the cover and sacophagus by covering them with thin plates of metal. The grooves into which strips of metal were forced with the same object may be noted.

Fig. 31: The sarcophagus of Seti I *Photograph: Gordon H Roberton*

The cover and the sarcophagus are ornamented inside and out with scenes from a very ancient Egyptian religious work, now generally known as "The Book of the Gates", or "The Book of the Pylons". The figures and scenes and the hieroglyphics were originally inlaid with a light greenish-blue composition which was made from sulphate of copper but the dampness of the English climate has caused the fillings of most of the characters to drop out and the originally brilliant white alabaster has become of a yellowish-brown tint through smoke. The "Book of the Gates" was written and illustrated with the view of teaching the pious Egyptians who worshipped Osiris and Ra the manner of the region through which their soul would pass after death, and the character of the beings whom they would meet there; in short, the work was intended to be a Guide to the Underworld. The name given to the Underworld by the Egyptians was "Tuat", and it was supposed to consist of a long, narrow valley, which ran towards the north, parallel with Egypt, but to the left of it, and then, sweeping eastwards in a curve, it continued its course on the right of the country, towards the south. When the sun set on this world, he was supposed to enter the Tuat at the end on the west and to emerge from it at the end on the east. The Tuat may be said to have been divided into twelve sections, which were, practically, identified with the twelve hours of the night; the first and last of these, however, were much smaller than the others, and served as antechambers, or vestibules. A river flowed through the Tuat, and it was chiefly by its means that the boat of the sun was able to make its way from one end of it to the other.

'*On the bottom of the sarcophagus,* inside, is the figure of the goddess Nut, to whose keeping the body of the dead King Seti I was committed. On each side of her are texts recording the names and titles of the king, and the speeches of the gods Seb and Nut. With these are versions of the seventy-second and eighty-ninth chapters of the "Book of the Dead".

'Four or five of the groups of scenes which form the representations of the divisions of the Tuat appear to belong to a very ancient magical work, which contained formulae and ceremonies for making the sun rise daily, and was probably in use among the predynastic inhabitants of Egypt.'

In the space surrounding the sarcophagus are various antique fragments, of which the following are the most important:

In west opening: niches to north and south, antique fragments (late 1st or 2nd century AD).

North side, west pier: death mask thought by Soane to be that of Parker, leader of the naval mutiny on the Nore in 1797, but perhaps that of Oliver Cromwell; fragment of a statue of the Aphrodite of Aphrodisias (M430: copy of a cult statue of the later Imperial period). *North side, under arch:* two busts on columns; left, a Roman private citizen of the Imperial second century, wearing a toga; right, a marble portrait bust of Polydeukes, the favourite of Herodes Atticus (Consul in 143 AD) wearing a Greek-style *himation* rather than a toga. (Herodes had homosexual affairs, of which the most famous was with the adolescent Polydeukes. When Polydeukes died, Herodes inaugurated a personality cult of his beloved, in imitation of the Emperor Hadrian who had posthumously proclaimed his lover, Antinous, a god). *On the floor, behind the north arch*: the wooden lid of an Egyptian coffin carved with a bearded face and wig with lappets (XIX–XXth Dynasty, *c*.150 BC; it was formerly in the Duke of Richmond's collection at Whitehall and was given to Soane by the architect John White); a Roman altar of the 2nd century AD, dedicated to Hercules. *North side, east pier*: fragment from a sarcophagus of the later Imperial period with figures of Cupid and Psyche. *In east opening: niche on north side*: fragment of alabaster chest for canopic jars, from the tomb of Seti I; fragment of the side of a Roman bench. *Niche on south side*: fragment of the leg of a Roman statue said to have been found in the Circus of Caracalla, Rome, 1819, by Sir Francis Chantrey and presented by him to Soane; fragment of a head of the Emperor Hadrian, from a large official relief (2nd century AD).

South side (high up on left): bare-breasted running Amazon, fragment of a Greek marble frieze (late 5th-century or early 4th-century BC).

South side, east pier: fragment of an antique alabaster vase (top); Roman marble bust of a man thought to date from the reign of the Emperor Antoninus Pius (138–161 AD) when short full beards were commonly worn in imitation of the Emperor (on column against pier).

South side, under arch: centre (front), Roman marble figure of Cupid (or Eros) asleep, seated on an urn. There is a hole through the mouth of the urn to the base, indicating that it was part of a fountain. The quality indicates that it was probably a garden sculpture, from a small fountain of the Antonine period (2nd century AD). Centre back, on a Corinthian capital on a taller column, a marble bust of a bearded man, of Greek marble, and dating from the Antonine period.

South side, west pier: marble bust of a young man with a short beard wearing a Greek *himation* and made of Greek marble, dating from the Antonine period (on column against pier).

THE EGYPTIAN CRYPT

Leaving the Sepulchral Chamber we pass eastwards into Soane's 'Egyptian Crypt', which, before the opening of the arch in the south wall (1891) was unlit and had a flat ceiling '*composed of massive blocks of stone*'. In the narrow passage to the right as we leave the Sepulchral Chamber hang slave shackles, described by Soane as '*implements of iron, to the honor of humanity no longer in use*'. On our left is a triple recess, through which light filters from above. In the left-hand compartment of this recess is a cork model of the temple of Fortuna Virilis in Rome, perhaps made in England in the late 18th century. To the right is a wooden model for a clock case, designed by Soane for the Bank of England. On the wall of the right-hand compartment are memorial tablets to Mrs Soane (d.1815) and John Soane, jun. (d.1823), the architect's eldest son. The tablet to Mrs Soane is inscribed with verses by a close friend, the novelist Mrs Barbara Hofland.

On the south side of the Crypt, facing the triple recess, is a large model of a statue of 'Britannia' which was submitted to a competition in 1799 by John Flaxman and exhibited at the Royal Academy in 1801. The statue, to be a national monument, was to have stood on Greenwich Hill and would have been 230 feet high. Within the arch, are standing figures of 'Faith' (with a cross) and 'Charity' (a mother with her children), models by Flaxman for the monument to Lady Spencer at Great Brington, Northants, c.1818.

To the east, beneath the opening leading to the staircase, are two casts of the Venus di Medici, the original of which is in the Uffizi Gallery, Florence. Flanking the opening are fluted columns over which are placed Corinthian capitals from the ruins of the Emperor Hadrian's Villa at Tivoli (2nd-century AD). Over these again are 18th-century wooden pilaster capitals from Sir Robert Taylor's halls at the Bank of England, demolished by Soane. In a niche to the right is an equestrian stature of George III by Peter Turnerelli.

We now ascend the stairs by the Monk's Parlour and return to the ground floor where we can proceed through 'The Colonnade' on our way to 'The Dome'.

THE MUSEUM

This was the title bestowed on the whole of the rear ground floor area by Soane. It is designed in a highly original way. Ten Corinthian columns serve to support the floor of the Students' Room or Upper Drawing Office which, as previously noted (p.18), does not come into contact with the main walls. Light is, therefore, admitted from above, on either side, as well as from the dome beyond and from the window looking into the Monument Court. '*The effect in this part*', wrote Soane, '*is rather solemn than gloomy, and the pictorial breaks of light and shade will be duly appreciated by the students and lovers of art*'.

Soane was partly enabled to execute his ingenious designs for this area by the fact that his system of central heating by means of hot pipes dispensed with the need for solid walls for fireplaces and stoves.

THE COLONNADE

On either side, between the columns, are the cupboards which originally housed some of the 54 volumes of drawings by Robert and James Adam acquired in 1833. These volumes are now kept in the Research Library with the rest of the Architectural Drawings Collection. The cupboards have been made using carved panels in the style associated with William Kent; these may have been among the furnishings removed by Soane from Walpole House in Chelsea (see pp.39 and 64). On these cupboards stand various marbles and casts.

South side, moving from east to west: a female torso (wearing a chiton) from the frieze of the Erechtheion at Athens (5th century BC) mounted on an oblong marble base. (Soane was not aware of the source of this important piece which was identified in 1927 by the eminent scholar Bernard Ashmole); model after the

Fig. 33: Roman marble statue of Aesculapius on the south side of the Colonnade.
Photograph: Geremy Butler

Fig. 34: The
Colonnade South
passage, looking east
*Photograph: Martin
Charles*

recumbant figure of 'Theseus' from the Elgin marbles, by Henry Rossi. A carved
Maori spear, in Soane's collection by 1822 and described as 'a grotesquely carved
walking stick' (fixed to upright pier). Statue of Aesculapius, a Roman 2nd-century
AD variation of a Greek original, formerly in the collection of Cardinal Polignac.
Above the Aesculapius on a high shelf is a plaster bust of Napoleon after Chaudet.

North side, moving from west to east: the Ephesian Diana. The torso only is
antique. This statue, incorporating the remains of a Roman copy of a famous
Greek temple image, was known as far back as the middle of the 16th century
when it was was in the collection of Cardinal Rudolfo Pio and it may previously
have been in the collection of Pope Julius III at the Villa Giulia in Rome.
Within the pedestal of the Diana is a Roman table-leg. Behind the Diana are two
fragments of Greek 4th-century BC sepulchral reliefs. To the right of the Diana
are plaster models of Michelangelo's reclining figures of 'Twilight' and 'Day' in
the Medici Chapel, S. Lorenzo, Florence. On the cupboard to the right is a model
of the figure of 'Ilissus' from the Elgin marbles, by Henry Rossi; cast of a head
of the goddess Diana, 'from the original found at Bath'; cast of the head of a
faun. To the left of the cupboard, on a pedestal is a plaster model by Flaxman,

Fig. 35:
Fragment of the frieze of the
Erechtheion, Athens, marble
*Photograph: Professor Margaret
Harker*

*c.*1808–09, for the statue of William Pitt, commissioned by the City of Glasgow.

On the North wall (behind): Coade Stone head of Neptune *c.*1775 and a Roman female mask from a fountain or bath.

SOUTH PASSAGE

In the window recess, to the left of the window '*is placed the model of a villa designed for Thomas Swinnerton, Esq. at Butterton Hall, Staffordshire*' *c.*1816. '*Under the model is a case containing eight drawers filled with fair drawings of Architectural Designs . . . and above . . . is a Model . . . of the Statue in St Paul's Cathedral of the late Sir Joshua Reynolds, P.R.A.*' by Flaxman, *c.*1807. The marble statue based on this model was placed in St Paul's in 1813.

On the east (left) wall of the window-recess is the torso of a statuette after the Doryphoros of Polycleitos. On the west (right) are two marble heads – fragments of the lost relief decoration of Trajan's Forum in Rome. On the north side of the passage are a small plaster version of the Laocoön and, below this (fixed to

Fig. 36: Roman marble statue
of the Ephesian Diana on the
north side of the Colonnade
Photograph: Ole Woldbye

the cupboard) medieval tiles from Chertsey Abbey. To the left, on shelves, are numerous antique fragments including (at floor level) two enriched tripod bases and a fragment of a marble vase decorated with four dancing amorini (far left, numbered 586).

The window provides a view of the upper part of the *pasticcio*, composed of a 'Norman' capital and a series of Soanean elements topped with a cast-iron finial (see p. 42). The lamp on the windowsill is a recreation (2003) of the gas lamp that Soane had in this position.

Proceeding westwards, we pass from the dimly lit Colonnade into the brightly lit portion of the Museum known as 'The Dome', *'lighted from the roof, and marked in its architectural decoration by a rich variety of outline and classical ornaments from the antique'.*

THE DOME

This is the oldest part of the present Museum, having been built in 1808–09 as a 'model room' or '*plaister room*', annexed to Soane's office at the back of No. 12. There is not, strictly speaking, a dome, though pendentives bring the square central space to a circle which, in turn, is covered by a conical skylight. Until 1833 the 'Dome' was a more elaborate and 'Picturesque' structure, raised on a circular glazed drum and filled with blue, crimson and yellow glass. In that year Soane altered it, removing the drum and simplifying the shape. This second plainer Soane 'Dome', took the same form as that which can be seen today. The small lean-to and triangular skylights above the Dome passages are filled with yellow glass. Mrs Hofland, who provided additional comments in Soane's own *Description* of 1835, described 'that exquisite distribution of light and colour which, often from undiscovered sources, sheds the most exquisite hues, and produces the most magical effects, throughout the Museum, thereby communi-

Fig. 37: The Dome Area looking east,
watercolour by J M Gandy, 1811
Photograph: Geremy Butler

cating the only charm in which an assembly of marbles must be deficient', i.e. the coloured glass shed a warm, romantic light over the marbles and casts which were otherwise white – and therefore lacking the charm that the possession of colour imparts. In the centre of the dome is a plaster rose which is subtly illuminated from behind by light coming in through small panes of red and orange glass. Mrs Hofland, commenting on the magical effects created by light from unexpected sources, noted that 'the ornament which crowns the inside of the dome is a remarkable proof of this, light from below being so thrown upon it as to render it of a pearl-like hue, and perfectly defined; whereas under common circumstances, it would have been in darkness'.

The central space of the Dome area connects with the Sepulchral Chamber below, the opening from the one to the other being protected by a balustrade, upon which stand a number of busts and vases. The balustrade has been cleaned to reveal Soane's original pink and green marbled finishes – preserved under layers of later varnish. On the piers of the Dome and the surrounding walls is a great

Fig. 38: Detail of the Dome Area looking east towards the bust of Sir John Soane by Sir Francis Chantrey
Photograph: Martin Charles

Fig. 39: Detail of the Dome Area looking north
Photograph: Geremy Butler

variety of objects, including antique fragments, casts and some works by Soane's contemporaries.

As we enter the Dome from the Colonnade '*a view into the Breakfast Room*' (through doors to the left) '*offers some striking effects of light and shade. The eye is also attracted to the cast of the Apollo Belvedere*' at the further end. Soane states that this cast was made for Lord Burlington and placed in his villa at Chiswick. During some alterations at the villa under the 5th Duke of Devonshire, the cast was given to the architect John White, who in turn presented it to Soane in 1811. '*I set so much value upon it*', says Soane, '*as to take down a large portion of the external wall in order to admit it into its present position*'. Soane had to make another opening in the north wall of the Dome to bring in the sarcophagus in 1824. The four vices bolted through the corner columns of the Dome may relate to its installation.

Directly opposite the Apollo and standing on the balustrade is the marble bust of Sir John Soane, presented to him by his friend, the sculptor Sir Francis Chantrey, in 1829. Soane began sitting for this bust in May 1827 and it was finished by 5 April 1829, when Chantrey wrote: 'Whether the bust . . . shall be considered John Soane or Julius Caesar is a point that cannot be determined by either you or me. I will however, maintain that as a work of art I have never produced a better.' The bust was exhibited in the Royal Academy in 1830. Soane was able to return Chantrey's compliment by designing the Ante-Room to the Sculpture Gallery at his house in Belgrave Place in 1830–31.

The bust stands on a lion-headed monopodium, on either side of which are statuettes, by Flaxman, of Michelangelo and Raphael, models for figures made for the painter, Sir Thomas Lawrence, about 1826. They came to the Museum as a gift from Flaxman's sister-in-law, Maria Denman (see pp.14–15), immediately after Soane's death and were placed here according to a wish he had expressed to associate the work of Flaxman and Chantrey in this way. Lawrence, too, shares in the association of prominent artists of Soane's day, for a plaster copy of the bust by Sievier (see p. 3) is seen high up in an opening from the Upper Drawing Office.

Of the many Classical antiquities displayed in this part of the Museum the following are noteworthy:

Balustrades. The cinerary vases are mainly antique but heavily restored in the 18th century. They were acquired at different times at the sales of the Bessborough, Mendip, Robert Adam and other collections. The busts are, likewise, largely restorations; exceptions are the life-size bust of a lady *c.*60 AD (probably a member of the Julio-Claudian imperial court) on the south balustrade (west end), and that of 'Augustus Caesar when a boy', a Roman copy after Polycleitos, similar to the 'Westmacott Athlete' in the British Museum, on the north (east end).

Below the west balustrade is a very fine and large Roman sarcophagus panel, formely in Robert Adam's collection, depicting The Rape of Proserpine. Below the north balustrade is a '*cast from an antique frieze in the Medici Garden*', and opposite, below the south balustrade, '*another of the festoon between the pilasters on the outside of the Pantheon*', Rome.

Piers. Among various marble and terracotta fragments fixed to the piers are two Roman fragments of sculptured sarcophagus fronts (east side).

North wall (Fig.39). In the centre, (top) two circular '*basso-relievos . . . allegorical of the morning and evening of the Roman Empire: between these works is another basso-relievo brought from Italy by the late Robert Adam*' depicting the Emperor Hadrian 'departing for the chase'. All the reliefs are modelled in plaster after reliefs on the Arch of Constantine in Rome. Immediately below is a cast of a portion of a Roman frieze of acanthus scrolls. Below this, a panel of scroll-ornament (Italian 15th-century). Below again, a portion of a small marble frieze showing youths chasing deer and an architrave. On the wall to the right (east end) is '*a cast of a basso-relievo by Flaxman, of "Mercury conveying Pandora to Epimetheus" and a cast from one of the compartments of the bronze Gates of St John's Baptistery at Florence (called, from Michael Angelo's compliment, the Gates of Paradise), the subject of which is "Giving the law"; it is the work of Lorenzo Ghiberti. Under this is a very beautiful model of a large salver; and a marble Cornucopia, highly ornamented, found in the Villa Adriana*'. (Hadrian's villa at Tivoli, near Rome: this item was probably part of a life-size female statue.)

South wall: A Roman marble pilaster capital from the original attic of the Pantheon in Rome (2nd-century AD; see p.100) and a cast of the same capital. Above the central doorway is a cast of part of the frieze of the Temple of Antoninus and Faustina in the Forum in Rome.

East wall. On either side of the centre opening to the Colonnade, in the recesses just above the floor, are two cinerary urns. That on the right, heavily restored, was in the collection of G B Piranesi.

Behind the Apollo is a small lobby which until the erection of the New Picture Room was a recess lined with bookcases, two of which survive. The slanted openings to this lobby are faced with mirror-glass alternating with dark ruby-coloured glass. Grilles in the floor allow light to penetrate into the Crypt below. In the pedestal of the Apollo is a small folding table which runs out on castors, at which Soane could sit when he wished to consult books in this part of his library. This arrangement was first and foremost a practical one but, although he was immensely proud to own Lord Burlington's cast of the famous Apollo Belvedere, he may well have derived some amusement from tucking this little table into the socle of such a celebrated statue. To the right of the arch opening into the New Picture Room is a self-portrait of John Flaxman at the age of 24, 1770, from the original wax now in the Victoria and Albert Museum.

NEW PICTURE ROOM

This room lies behind the Apollo and the small lobby just mentioned. Built in 1889–90 to the design of James Wild (Curator 1878–92), it stands on the site of Soane's original office, behind No. 12. Soane later used the original room as a Library and then, in 1819, it became his first Picture Room. Soane himself walled off this room in about 1824 and it formed part of No. 12 Lincoln's Inn Fields until the termination of a lease of these premises in 1889, when it was rebuilt as an extension of the Museum, allowing for the more adequate display of certain paintings and sculptures. The works of art shown here are as follows:

Facing the entrance is a large painting by Canaletto, a view of the *Riva degli*

Fig. 40: View of the *Riva degli Schiavoni,* Venice, by Canaletto *Photograph: Prudence Cuming Associates*

Schiavoni in Venice with St Mark's, the Doge's Palace and the entrance to the Grand Canal in the background (Fig.40). This was formerly in the Calonne collection in Paris and later belonged to William Beckford; Soane bought it at the sale of the contents of Fonthill Splendens in 1807. Above hangs an early portrait of John Soane (aged 22 or 23) by C W Hunneman, painted in 1776, the same year that Soane won the Royal Academy Gold Medal for Architecture.

Below is a remarkable set of ivory furniture from Southern India, dating from about 1790. Soane seems to have acquired this by 1823 and stated that it was among the belongings of Tipú Sultán (called Tipoo Sahib by the English) which were captured at the siege of Seringapatam in 1799 when Tipú was killed. This provenance is attached to a number of similar pieces of ivory furniture in British collections but is now thought to be spurious. The chairs and table were almost certainly manufactured in Murshidabad in Bengal. On the table is a cork model of the Temple of Vesta at Tivoli. It is signed by Giovanni Altieri and dated '177–'.

To the right is a small table which belonged to Mrs Soane. The top is set with samples of marble and other stones which may possibly have been brought back from Rome by Soane when he visited the city as a young man in 1778–79. This table was specially made by Foxhall in 1808 to take Soane's existing marble top. In Soane's day it occupied a prominent position in Mrs Soane's small Morning

Fig. 41: 'The Passage Point – An Italian Composition' by Sir A W Callcott *Photograph: Geremy Butler*

Room, now the Secretary's office, on the second floor. Near this table is a hand-some late 17th-century long-case clock with seaweed marquetry decoration, the movement bearing the name of William Threlkeld. Above this hang two more Venetian scenes by Canaletto, one of the Piazza S. Marco and the other of the Rialto Bridge from the north (Fig.42), both of which came from the Bute collection (sold in 1796). Soane was especially proud of these pictures and had them in his apartment at Chelsea Hospital before bringing them to this building. To the right of the Canalettos hangs a fine pillar barometer by Daniel Quare, clockmaker of London, *c.*1695.

On the left (south) wall, is a large picture that was commissioned by Soane in 1829, 'The Passage Point – an Italian composition' by A W Callcott, which was exhibited at the RA in 1830 (Fig.41). Soane commissioned Callcott to produce this work for him after rejecting Turner's 'Forum Romanum for Mr. Soane's Museum' (now in the Tate) which he had commissioned in 1828 for £500. Apparently Soane handed Callcott a 'strange letter' enclosing £500 and giving him the commission at a dinner party in 1829. He probably asked specifically for the Temple of Vesta at Tivoli to be included (far right). Soane may have rejected Turner's painting on stylistic grounds rather than because of its size, since Callcott's picture is larger. In Soane's lifetime the painting hung on the north wall of the Picture Room, inside the planes.

The desk below was probably obtained by Soane from Lord Yarborough's house, formerly Walpole House, Chelsea, on the demolition of that building in 1811 for the new Infirmary of the Royal Hospital. It is said to have belonged to

Fig. 42: The Rialto Bridge from the North by Canaletto *Photograph: Prudence Cuming Associates*

Sir Robert Walpole and dates from about 1735.

The two plaster eagles on either side of the archway formed part of the decoration of the entrance to the staircase at Carlton House (see p.44). Below them (behind curtains) are two portraits by John Downman: on the left John Soane, jun. and on the right Mrs Soane, sen., the mother of Sir John Soane, aged 84. A selection of books for sale is on display in this room. On leaving the New Picture Room turn right to pass through a doorway into the Ante-Room.

THE ANTE-ROOM

This is approached via a narrow lobby spanned by a long, half-round skylight filled with pale yellow glass. This lobby was Soane's original Ante-Room, modified and extended in 1889–90 to the designs of James Wild, the then Curator, who took down much of the south wall to create the opening into his new Ante-Room, for which he adopted the Moorish style of decoration. The space occupied by this room in fact lies partly in what had been the back yard of No. 12 Lincoln's Inn Fields, Soane's earlier residence (see p.67). When Soane lived at No. 12 a passageway led from that house through this area and across to Soane's office which lay where the New Picture Room was subsequently erected (see p.62).

On the walls at either end of the lobby are casts of medallions, after the bas-reliefs on the Arch of Constantine, by Thomas Banks, used by Soane in the

Lothbury Court of the Bank of England, 1801. Below the medallion on the west is a plaster cast of the 'Taddei tondo' of the Virgin and Child by Michelangelo (the original marble is in the Royal Academy of Arts, London).

The table below this, in the style of William Kent and a pair to one in the Monk's Parlour (p.39), came from Lord Yarborough's house in Chelsea. On the table are a pair of lead figures of slaves after Pietro Tacca. The table-top, set with marble samples, is not original to the table. Beneath the table, on the floor, is a section of Roman mosaic pavement.

In the glass cupboard to the right of the table is a selection of domestic china used by Sir John Soane and an elephant's tooth (numbered A51) dug up in Burma during the war of 1826. Above the cupboard is another work by Thomas Banks, 'Camadeva and his Mistress on a Crocodile' (probably executed about 1792), a cast given to Soane by the sculptor.

To the left of the opening to Wild's Moorish Ante-Room hang two small oil paintings, Indian scenes, by William Daniell (both exhib. RA 1832).

On the east (left) side of the Wild Ante-Room are two display cases. The left-hand one contains a selection of small objects which in Soane's day were displayed on shelves and tables throughout the house. These include an 18th-century fake Egyptian bronze, an Egyptian black steatite figure of the god Ma clad in a leopard skin (xxv Dynasty) and a figure of the lioness-headed goddess Sekhmet (xviii or xix Dynasty). The right-hand case contains three works by John Flaxman: a charming portrait medallion of his wife Ann (Nancy) (a duplicate of the framed medallion on the Staircase but with a tinted ground (see p.83)); a plaster cast of a portrait medallion by Flaxman of himself aged 14, 1769, given to Soane by Flaxman's sister-in-law, Maria Denman, and a wax model by Flaxman of the bronze torso of the Hercules Hesperides in the British Museum. On the shelf below is a case containing 18 chessmen modelled for Wedgwood by Flaxman with characters from Macbeth and another containing a cork model of the Arch of Constantine, purchased by Soane at John Govan's Sale in 1804 for £37 16s.

On the west (right) wall in a showcase are more small objects from Soane's collection. They include a series of Italian 16th-century bronze heads of Roman Emperors, an Egyptian xxvi Dynasty bronze uraeus (cobra with spread hood) and Egyptian faience ushabti (servant) figures (xxi–xxii Dynasty, xxvi Dynasty and xxvii–xxix Dynasty). On the shelf below is a case containing a selection of keys (including Soane's key to Lincoln's Inn Fields) and a rosary, with attached miniature skull and cross inlaid with mother-of-pearl, brought back from Rome in 1794 by Mrs Flaxman.

NO. 12 LINCOLN'S INN FIELDS

From the Ante-Room the narrow link passage leads through to No. 12 Lincoln's Inn Fields. This house was built by Soane for his own occupation in 1792–93 and he lived here until the building of the Museum (No. 13) 20 years later. He retained the ownership of No. 12 and at his death left it as part of the endowment of the Museum. It was leased to a series of tenants until 1969 when the Trustees entered into possession and obtained powers to restore and equip the house as an extension of the Museum. It opened as such in 1971.

The history of No. 12 is as follows:

In 1792, Soane bought the old house on the site for £2,100 and demolished it. He then rebuilt it to his own design. At the back, where the previous house had stables opening on to Whetstone Park, Soane instead created an architect's office from which he ran his practice. The builders of the new house were men whom Soane was employing at the Bank of England where his first series of halls was in progress. The house was finished in the summer of 1793 and the Soane family took up residence in January 1794. The Soanes lived here from 1794 until 1813, when they moved into the larger house (No. 13) which Soane had built next door

Fig. 43: The Soane family having breakfast in the Breakfast Parlour, No. 12, watercolour by J M Gandy, November 1798
Photograph: Geremy Butler

and which was to become the Soane Museum. It was in No. 12 that he started to assemble his collection, and after 1806, when he was appointed Professor of Architecture at the Royal Academy, he began to think of arranging and expanding it for the benefit of his students. In May 1807 Soane wrote to his neighbour, George Booth Tyndale to ask if he might purchase the stable block at the back of No. 13 and saying that he was prepared to purchase the whole No. 13 property in order to acquire it. In June 1808 the sale of No. 13 was completed and Soane proceeded to demolish the stable block at the rear and build what is now the Dome area of the Museum (p.58). Meanwhile, Tyndale continued to live in the front part of No. 13 until 1812 when Soane demolished it. Tyndale then took a lease of No. 12, Soane rebuilding No. 13 as it now exists.

Tyndale, who was an antiquary and a hereditary Trustee of the British Museum, lived in No. 12 until 1826. The house was then taken on lease by Edward Stanley, a distinguished surgeon and a future President of the Royal College of Surgeons. He surrendered his lease in 1843 when the house was taken by Edward Whitaker, a solicitor. The firm of Whitaker and Woolbert was occupying the house in 1900 when their business failed and Francis Whitaker committed suicide. From 1900 to 1969, No. 12 was continuously occupied by firms of solicitors. The freehold remained in the hands of the Trustees of Sir John Soane's Museum, in whom it had been vested at Soane's death by the Act of 1833 (see pp.102 & 127) as part of the Museum endowment.

The passage through to No. 12 from the Ante-Room is the only surviving section of Soane's original passage linking the front and back of No. 12. It now contains a showcase in which are displayed small and precious items from Soane's collection. These include antique and neo-classical gems, the Gold Medal presented to Soane by 'the Architects of England' in 1835 in recognition of his outstanding contribution to the profession, a ceremonial gold key bearing the cipher of King William and Queen Mary c.1690s, a chronometer by Thomas Mudge and miniatures of Soane, his wife Elizabeth and their close friend Nancy Storace (the singer who was Mozart's first Susanna in 'The Marriage of Figaro').

The two rooms on the ground floor were Soane's Dining Room (the front room) and Breakfast Parlour.

The main feature of the Breakfast Parlour is the vaulted ceiling decorated with a painted design of trellis, honeysuckle and columbine, as if the room were open to the sky like a pergola. The ceiling was painted for Soane by John Crace the elder. Covered for many years with paint and whitewash, the original paintwork was uncovered in 1970 and further restored in 1993 with the help of a generous grant from Sir John Soane's Museum Foundation, New York. The room is now arranged to correspond as far as possible with a watercolour by J M Gandy of November 1798, showing the Soane family at breakfast (Fig.43, p.67).

The bookcases on the east wall and the mirror over the fireplace are original to the room. The rest of the furniture, the upholstery and the carpet have been reproduced to re-create exactly what is shown in Gandy's watercolour. On the west (fireplace) wall hang engravings by G B Piranesi from his *Vedute di Roma*. On the east wall above the bookcases further Piranesi engravings flank Soane's own drawing of the Banqueting House, Whitehall, which won him the Silver Medal of the RA in 1772. A design for a ceiling for the Palazzo Borghese by Mario Asprucci and a drawing of the 'celebrated antique mosaic pavement found at Otricoli now in the grand, circular saloon of the Vatican', by C H Tatham, flank the convex mirror. In a niche high up on the wall to the left of the fireplace is a small plaster figure of the Farnese Hercules. In a niche above the door to the Hall is a plaster figure of Flora, painted to resemble terracotta, modelled by Rysbrack after the celebrated antique statue the 'Farnese Flora' in the Museo Nazionale in Naples. On the south side of the room are two plaster models by François Fouquet, the Temple of Augustus at Pola, Istria, and a mausoleum (the Temple of Neptune) at Palmyra.

The adjacent front room, originally Soane's Dining Room (and painted an 'Etruscan' red at that time), is now the 'Soane Gallery', with showcases designed by Eva Jiricna (1995), in which changing exhibitions of drawings from Soane's collection are mounted.

THE BREAKFAST PARLOUR (NO. 13 LINCOLN'S INN FIELDS)

Returning to No. 13 via the Link Passage and leaving the Ante-Room through the door to the right we enter the Breakfast Parlour. This room, built with the rest of the front of No. 13 in 1812, is a highly characteristic example of Soane's personal style. '*In the centre*', says the *Description* of 1835, '*rises a spherical ceiling, springing from four segmental arches, supported by the same number of pilasters, forming a rich canopy. The spandrels of the dome and the soffits of the arches are decorated with a number of mirrors. In the dome is an octangular lantern-light, enriched with eight Scriptural subjects in painted glass. At the north and south ends of the room are skylights, which diffuse strong lights over the several Architectural and other works decorating the walls*'. To this note, Soane adds the following clue to his own feelings about the room: '*The view from this room into the Monument Court and into the Museum, the mirrors in the ceiling, and the looking-glass, combined with the variety of outline and general arrangements in the design and decoration of this limited space, present a succession of those fanciful effects which constitute the poetry of Architecture.'*

This room was entirely redecorated in 1951, on the basis of remains of the original finish discovered under successive repaintings. The coloured glass in the central lantern is seen to its best advantage in strong afternoon sunlight when rainbow effects may be seen cast on the walls of the room and across the courtyard. The two skylights are filled with yellow coloured glass. In the south skylight are two panels of 17th-century stained glass: 'St Elizabeth of Hungary giving alms to a beggar' and a monk or hermit receiving a royal or saintly visitor (perhaps also St Elizabeth of Hungary). In the small window the lower pane of glass was originally etched, presumably to hide the earthenware pots of the shrubs outside.

The principal contents of the Breakfast Parlour are as follows:

On the back marble fireplace are three plaster busts by Flaxman: Left, William Hayley (*c.*1781); centre, the sculptor's father; right, the artist Henry Howard. Also by Flaxman are the three plaques, under yellow glass, set into the front face of the

Fig. 44: The Breakfast Parlour, No. 13, looking north *Photograph: Martin Charles*

Fig. 45: 'The Contention of Oberon and Titania', a scene from *A Midsummer Night's Dream*, by Henry Howard, oil on canvas, 1832
Photograph: Prudence Cuming Associates

fireplace. The central plaque was modelled for a vase presented to Dr W S Goddard, headmaster of Winchester College from 1806 to 1809. The plaques to left and right were modelled for a vase presented to J P Kemble on his retirement from the stage, 1817. They represent (*left*) 'Kemble crowned by Melpomene' and (*right*) 'Kemble inspired by the genius of Shakespeare'.

On the upper shelf, in a glass case, is a small bronze lion flanked by (*left*) a small Roman bronze Lar and (*right*) a figure of a philosopher by Flaxman; the group was assembled by Flaxman and came to Soane through Maria Denman. Also on this shelf (*right*) is a Roman alabaster table-leg balanced by a plaster copy on the left.

Above the bookcase on the north side of the room is a cast from an antique bronze Victory, now in the Museum at Kassel, in Germany. It was procured by Flaxman in Rome, given to Soane by Maria Denman in 1836 and fixed here under Soane's direction on 10 January 1837, ten days before his death. Behind this figure is a watercolour of the Soane family tomb (see p.148) while to the left and right are coloured engravings by Angelo Campanella of mural decoration in the ruins of a Classical Roman villa discovered in the grounds of the Villa Negroni not long before Soane arrived in Rome in 1778. The discovery caused a sensation at the time and evidently impressed Soane who acquired two sets of these engravings, which were published between 1778 and 1802. Soane's early patron, the Bishop of Derry, with whom he travelled in Italy, purchased several of the original frescoes which he intended to install at Downhill, his seat in Ireland, so Soane would have had a first-hand knowledge of them. The decoration of Soane's Library and Dining Room (see p.4) suggests that, more than a quarter of a century later, Soane was deriving a measure of inspiration from this colourful source.

In a recess to the left are three Soane drawings: the interior of Messrs Thellusson's counting-house (*c.*1810–11) and two early studies for Tyringham, Bucks. (*c.*1793).

On either side of the window are cabinets, with pictures both outside and within, as follows: On the *outer planes* are two more coloured prints by Campanella of the Villa Negroni mural decorations. Above these are engravings by William Woollett from Landscapes by Dughet and Glauber (Polydor), while below are two portraits of the Soane household pet Fanny – *(left)* a watercolour drawing by Van Assen; *(right)* a posthumous portrait by James Ward, 1822, in which the Erechtheion in Athens can be seen in the background (see p.30).

Within the doors of the cabinets are drawings of ceilings, based on originals in the ruins of Rome. In the left-hand cabinet are two further engravings of the Villa Negroni frescoes, while in the right-hand cabinet are the following: 'David Garrick as Cardinal Wolsey' (in fact a mezzotint of Garrick's death-mask by R E Pine, 1779); Chelsea Old Church, 1815 (watercolour by John Denham) and a portrait of Giovanni Belzoni the discoverer of the Seti sarcophagus (lithograph signed Fabroni, 1824).

On the jambs of the window, besides engraved portraits of four of Soane's contemporaries, are some exquisite miniature paintings, purchased by Soane from J Sainsbury in 1835 as by a French artist named 'Labelle'. In fact, the artist was Jean-François Lebelle (d.1830), although at least four of the smaller scenes (two hunting scenes and two landscapes with figures in 17th-century dress) are signed by Charles Bellier (b.1796). The small paintings are said to be painted on silk and attached to glass while the larger ones are on canvas, again attached to glass. Most of them probably show imaginary ruins and townscapes although Sainsbury claimed that two depicted the interiors of the cathedrals of Rheims and Milan.

Between the mirror-faced doors in the south wall is a niche made to hold an important clock by Benjamin Lewis Vulliamy who was clock-maker to the King. Note how the hood of the case, almost certainly designed by Soane, echoes the shallow dome of the room and contains small lunettes of yellow glass.

Above hangs 'The Contention of Oberon and Titania' (Shakespeare's *A Midsummer Night's Dream,* Act II, Scene 1), painted by Henry Howard (exhib. RA 1832) see Fig.45. On either side are designs by Soane for the vestibule in his House of Lords design of 1794 (probably two of the many views of this design exhibited in the Royal Academy between 1801 and 1814), while in the right-hand corner is a view of the Prince's Street entrance of the Bank of England.

Below is Rysbrack's model in terracotta for the (larger) marble panel on the

Duke of Marlborough's tomb at Blenheim Palace (1732). The subject is the Surrender of Tallard to the Duke of Marlborough after the Battle of Blenheim. The defeated French troops (on the right) are about to surrender their colours (flags) to the victorious British (on the left). The two Field Marshals face each other in the centre, at the head of their men.

On the same wall are a group of Napoleonic exhibits (Soane was evidently an admirer of Napoleon). To the right of the clock is a miniature of the Emperor by Isabey, taken at Elba when he was in exile. This was given by the Baron d'Este to Sir William Beechey, RA, the painter. Lady Beechey lent it to Soane in 1830 and after her death in 1835 Sir William presented it to him. The other portrait of Napoleon (left) shows him in his twenty-eighth year, and is said to have been painted by an Italian artist, Cossia, at Verona in 1797. A pistol that Soane believed had belonged to Napoleon was stolen in 1969. The pistol case remains on display to maintain the composition arranged by Soane on this wall.

It is noteworthy that Soane owned a cast (rather a poor one, unfortunately) of Donatello's bronze 'Chellini Madonna' which has been in the Victoria & Albert Museum since 1976. When this cast was made it was in private hands in England. Interestingly, Soane knew this cast was from a work by Donatello. Later, this information was lost and the original was only rediscovered by scholars in the 1970s. This and the cast of a Greek bronze relief (c.400 BC, discovered in 1792 at Paramythia and now in the British Museum) were both presented to Soane by Henry Howard, RA, the painter whom Soane so liberally patronised, and hang on either side of the niche containing the clock.

THE STAIRCASE AND THE SHAKESPEARE RECESS

We now ascend to the first floor via the staircase (see also pp.4 and 82). Soane's stair-carpet has been re-created (1990) following the evidence of several water-colour views made in the 1820s.

On the left we pass a niche containing a plaster model by John Flaxman, 'St Michael defeating Satan' (1822, for the marble at Petworth House, Sussex). On the wall is a large picture, painted in Rome by James Durno for Alderman Boydell's Shakespeare Gallery in Pall Mall and bought by Mrs Soane for 9 guineas at the sale of the Gallery in 1805. It represents 'Falstaff in disguise led out by Mrs Page' (*Merry Wives of Windsor*, Act IV Scene 2).

At the turn of the stairs we reach 'The Shakespeare Recess'. Such shrines to the Bard were not uncommon in Soane's day. The bust of Shakespeare is a cast by George Bullock, 1814, of the bust on the poet's monument at Stratford and is one

Fig. 46:
The Staircase looking up
to the Shakespeare Recess
Photograph:
Martin Charles

of a small series produced by Bullock and sold to various antiquarians including John Britton. When the recess was restored in 1990, the mirrored cupboard, which in Soane's day provided storage space for a blue and white Chinese export dinner service, was rebuilt. The walls were re-marbled and now demonstrate accurately what the whole of the staircase would have looked like in Soane's day. The ceiling was also re-created based on watercolours from 1825 and 1830. The sash-window originally contained an arrangement of stained glass.

The two paintings on the left are by Henry Howard. *Above;* 'Lear and Cordelia' (exhib. RA 1820). *Below:* 'The Vision of Shakespeare', commissioned in 1830 and described by Soane as follows: ' *"The Vision of Shakespeare".* . . *represents the bard resting on the lap of Fancy, contemplating the "visions of glory" which she invokes, while Lyrical Poetry, rising from the earth, invites him to ascend the brightest heaven of invention, Tragedy and Comedy are calling before him the shaowy forms of his principal dramatic characters: near him, Titania, watched by Oberon, is sleeping in her bower, and a train of fairies are sporting about him; on one side the stars are shooting from their spheres "to hear the sea-maid's music"; on the other side is the*

Tempest, the enchanted isle, and its inhabitants; above is Hecate riding on a cloud, and Genii, the offspring of Fancy, are hovering near her sweetest child.'

Adjoining the Shakespeare Recess is a triple-bay window on the staircase. Within the bay is a version of Giovanni Bologna's famous bronze Mercury in the Bargello at Florence. It is probably the work of Pietro Tacca, one of Bolgona's pupils and dates from the second quarter of the 17th century. Further on, in another recess, is a portrait bust in plaster of George Dance the younger, Soane's 'revered master', by J C F Rossi (probably exhib. RA 1825).

As we reach the first-floor landing, we see above the Drawing Room door an oval relief in plaster, 'The Judgement of Midas', for which the sculptor, Henry Webber, was awarded the Royal Academy Gold Medal in 1776, the year in which Soane received the corresponding award for architecture. In a high recess on the left is a plaster bust of the playwright and politician R B Sheridan by George Garrard (probably exhib. RA 1813).

THE DRAWING ROOMS

THE SOUTH DRAWING ROOM

On the first floor we now enter the Drawing Rooms. The present entrance leads into the South Drawing Room but the original entrance was from the Staircase into the North Drawing Room which Soane called 'The Anti-room' on early plans.

The South Drawing Room served as a library from 1919 to 1970 but when No. 12 (the adjoining house) became part of the Museum premises it became possible to remove the bookcases and presses and to reinstate the room almost exactly as Soane had it during his lifetime. Most of the original furniture can now be seen here. Lacking are a pair of Adam-style candlestands (sold by the Trustees shortly after Soane's death – quite improperly – see p.104) and the original chandelier (a modern reproduction hangs in its place). Both rooms were re-painted their original 'patent-yellow' in 1987, following paint sections taken by Dr Ian Bristow. The carpet has been re-created following the pattern shown in an engraving of 1835 and the curtains have been re-made as detailed in the original bill and as shown in watercolours drawn during Soane's lifetime.

Upon the South Drawing Room Soane's observations are as follows: *'The Ceiling is formed in domical compartments and flat surfaces, encircled with a variety of architectural decorations . . . [the west] end of the room makes an obtuse angle with the south side, to mask which irregularity it is made circular, and variety and convenience thereby produced. According to the original construction, this room was lighted from the south by three large windows opening into a loggia, commanding*

Fig. 47, left: The South Drawing Room in August 1825, watercolour by J M Gandy. Note the two black tripod stands either side of the fireplace, sold by the Trustees after Soane's death

Fig. 48, right: Pencil sketch of Mrs Soane by John Flaxman   *Photographs: Geremy Butler*

views of the gardens of Lincoln's Inn Fields, and decorated with Pillars, Busts, and Statues of eminent persons: this loggia has since [1834] *been enclosed, and now forms a Gallery extending the whole length of the room. The ceiling is formed in compartments, and the panels are enriched with Roses from the antique, and other Architectural decorations. Between the apertures are two recesses, in which are Casts from antique Candelabra in the Museo Vaticano. Over these apertures . . . are Basso relievos from the antique, typical of the Morning and Evening of Life . . . The boxings in which the shutters were formerly placed are filled in with bookcases, containing a variety of general and miscellaneous literature.'*

As with the Library downstairs, the projecting loggia was originally open and the windows were in line with the street frontage of the buildings on this side of the Square. Later Soane included the loggia as part of the internal space by glazing the arches, thus achieving the room's present conformation. The narrow windows at each end of the loggia were originally both fitted with stained glass subjects (one has been reconstructed; both were damaged during the War). A description of this room in *The Penny Magazine* of 30 November 1837, refers to the way in which 'On a summer evening, when the beams of the sun are playing through the coloured glass . . . every object is lit up "with gorgeous hues".'

Flanking the fireplace are portraits by William Owen of Soane *(right)* at the age of 51 and *(left)* of his two sons, John *(right)* and George *(left)*. Both were exhibited at the RA in 1805. On the mantelshelf are three pieces of dark red glazed Staffordshire pottery *c.*1800–10.

Fig. 49: The South Drawing Room
Photograph: Martin Charles

Opposite the fireplace, on the west wall, are small drawings for book-illustrations by E H Corbould and T Stothard. Above these hang two framed diplomas of the Royal Academy, the one on the right constituting Soane an Associate, November 1795, and the other, on the left, dated 8 April 1802, constituting him a full Royal Academician. The cupboard beneath was presumably designed by Soane, judging by its plain lines and lack of heavy mouldings but may be part of the 1920s furnishings of the Research Library. The veneer used for the front panels is particularly handsome. On it stands a chiming clock made by Thwaites and Reed, very similar to that in the Breakfast Room.

Turning to the window wall and loggia, we see, between the two right-hand openings into the loggia, a drawing of Mrs Soane (d.1815) by J Flaxman, probably drawn *c.*1795, presented to Soane by J M W Turner in 1831 (Fig. 47; see also p.30). Under the portrait hangs an inscription in French, identical to that on the model of Mrs Soane's tomb (p.7) '*Chere aimé, je ne peux plus entendre ta voix – apprends moi ce que je dois faire – pour remplir tes souhaits!*'. On the two side tables are Coalport ice-pails with drop-in bowls, to cool fruit, from a John Rose dessert service *c.*1805.

In each of the open arches are two high recesses above the bookcases containing models by John Flaxman as follows (left to right):

First arch. Kemble (*c.*1826 for the statue in Westminster Abbey) and a cast from

Fig. 50:
The Dance Cabinet
in the North
Drawing Room
Photograph:
Geremy Butler

a 15th-century statue of a king (Westminster Abbey).

Second arch. Marquis of Hastings (1826, for the statue at Calcutta) and the Younger Pitt (*c.*1808–09) for the statue at Glasgow see also pp.55 and 82).

Third arch. Joshua Reynolds (*c.*1803–07) and Warren Hastings.

Within the loggia and standing on the cross-beams are six plaster busts – three after antique models, one of Inigo Jones, one of Sir Christopher Wren and one a self-portrait by Flaxman.

Between the windows are the following drawings:

Left centre pier (behind the green curtain). Herman Saftleven, A Village Scene; Theodor van Thulden, design for an emblematic portrait frame said to have been intended to hold a portrait of King Charles I; Soane, *Geometrical elevations of the entablature and capital of the Temple* [of Vesta] *at Tivoli,* drawn from actual measurements while he was in Italy, 1779.

Right centre pier (behind the green curtain). Sepia drawing after Tintoretto's painting in S. Maria del 'Orto, Venice, 'The Golden Calf'(Soane thought this was by Veronese); *Elevation of the remains of the Temple* [of Vesta] *at Tivoli,* drawn by Soane in Italy, 1779.

Facing the windows, in niches, are two casts of Roman candelabra in the Vatican Museums.

On the north wall is an engraved portrait of Soane by Charles Turner after the Lawrence portrait (p.4). Over the door to the staircase is a watercolour by Frank Howard, son of Henry Howard, 'The Trial of Queen Katharine from Henry VIII, Act 2', purchased in 1833.

Pass through the double doors to enter the North Drawing Room.

THE NORTH DRAWING ROOM

This back Drawing Room served as an ante-room and subsidiary Drawing Room to the main room to the south. In the 1830s Soane installed movable planes between the windows (where previously there had been pier-glasses and tables) and on the walls opposite. The planes enabled him to display drawings and views of buildings he had designed, so the North Drawing Room became more like a gallery. The entrance door leading on to the staircase was converted into a bookcase in the 1920s.

'*The ceiling of this room*', says Soane, '*is partly groined and partly flat; a mode of decoration calculated to give variety and movement to the composition.*' It is a type of ceiling adopted by Soane about 1792 and used by him on many occasions in the course of his practice.

In the middle of the room stands the 'Dance Cabinet', on a base designed by Soane. The cabinet contains the collection of drawings by Soane's master, George Dance the younger and bears the following inscription: *This Cabinet enshrines a collection of Architectural Designs and Drawings of the late George Dance, Esq., R.A. and another by his pupil the founder of the Soane Museum.* It was acquired from the Dance family in 1836 and at the time of Soane's death stood in the Library. Hung on the west side of the cabinet are drawings of the Bank of England and of Soane's design of 1794 for the Houses of Parliament. On the south side is a general plan of the Bank dated 1831. Standing on the cabinet are models of antique buildings made in Paris by François Fouquet, acquired by Soane in 1834 (see p.87).

Over the fireplace (on the east wall) hangs a painting by Francis Danby, '*Scene from Shakespeare's The Merchant of Venice. Belmont – In the Garden of Portia's House. Lorenzo and Jessica. Lorenzo. . . "How sweet the Moonlight sleeps upon this bank,/Here will we sit and let the sounds of music/creep in our ears – soft stillness of the night/Become the torches of sweet Harmony/Sit Jessica, look how the floor of Heav'n/is thick inlaid with patterns of bright gold"*' (exhib. RA 1828). Soane commissioned this painting from Danby via Sir Francis Chantrey in May 1827 as a charitable gesture when Danby was in severe financial difficulties – and paid him £152 10s for it. Chantrey wrote to Soane that the first instalment 'came at a most fortunate moment – indeed, I have reason to think it may be the means of keeping him from sinking. I also believe that if he can hold out a little longer he will . . . recover the ground he has lost'. The bookcases on either side of the fireplace are modern (*c.*1920).

Opposite the fireplace hangs an important oil painting by J M W Turner, entitled 'Admiral Van Tromp's barge at the entrance of the Texel, 1645', which was

Fig. 51: Bird's-eye cut-away perspective of the Bank of England, watercolour
by J M Gandy, 1830 *Photograph: Geremy Butler*

exhibited at the RA in 1831 (Fig.52). It is in its original frame and has now been re-hung in its original position. Above (centre) is a watercolour drawing of the gateway to a Royal Palace (see pp.33 and 82) and two drawings of Soane's student design for a British Senate House, 1779. Below is a pair to the cupboard in the South Drawing Room.

In the cabinets between the windows are designs by Soane, most of them drawn by J M Gandy. The pictures are listed plane by plane, the upper picture being listed first.

Left-hand cabinet

Outside Plane: Royal Gallery, House of Lords, as executed (exhib. RA 1824); Court of Chancery, Westminster (exhib. RA 1827).

Inside Plane (left): Gallery in House of Lords: project of 1794 (exhib. RA 1809); Conference Room, House of Lords: project of 1794 (probably one of the many RA exhibits of 1801–09).

Inside Plane (right): Scala Regia, House of Lords: project of 1794 (exhib. RA 1803); Triumphal Bridge: the 1779 Parma version of Soane's Royal Academy Gold Medal design of 1776 (exhib. RA 1799; see pp.32 and 82).

Right-hand cabinet

Outside Plane: Entrance to the Scala Regia, House of Lords, as executed (exhib. RA 1823); The Court of King's Bench (exhib. RA 1827).

Inside Plane (left): Vestibule in the House of Lords: project of 1794(?);

Fig. 52: 'Admiral Van Tromp's barge at the entrance to Texel, 1645', by J M W Turner, oil on canvas, 1831
Photograph: Geremy Butler

Conference Room in the House of Lords: project of 1794 (probably one of the exhibits of 1801–09).

Inside Plane (right): Two views of a design for a Sepulchral Chapel to commemorate the Duke of York (exhib. RA 1828).

Above the left-hand cabinet is a design for Soane's House of Lords project of 1796 (exhib. RA in that year). Above the right-hand cabinet is a design for an entrance to Hyde Park (exhib. RA 1798).

On the window shelves are two cases containing a collection of Napoleonic medals, struck during the Consulate and Empire periods to celebrate victories and other events, under the direction of the noted antiquarian, Baron Denon, who is said to have made the selection for the Empress Josephine.

Opposite, on the south wall flanking the double doors, are two more cabinets containing:

Left-hand cabinet

Outside Plane: design for new House of Lords, 1794; plan of the same.

Inside Plane (left): Group of Churches to illustrate different styles of architecture (exhib. RA 1825); design for a Royal Palace – the portico (exhib. RA 1827; see pp.33 and 80).

Inside Plane (right): project for Whitehall, duplicating the existing Board of Trade and Privy Council Offices, to the west of Downing Street (exhib. RA 1836); Triumphal Bridge, copy of the original design awarded the Royal Academy Gold Medal in 1776.

Right-hand cabinet

Outside Plane: design for the Houses of Parliament and Law Courts (1796); plan of the same.

Inside Plane (left):design to extend north front of Westminster Hall to form the exterior of the Law Courts (exhib. RA 1829); Mausoleum and Picture Gallery, Dulwich College (exhib. RA 1812).

Inside Plane (right): Masonic Hall, Freemasons' Tavern, at night (exhib. RA 1832); Bank of England, bird's-eye view (often called 'The Bank in Ruins') exhib. RA 1830).

Over the doorway is a group of three sketches for a memorial to the Duke of York, 1829.

THE STAIRCASE TO THE UPPER FLOORS

We now return through the South Drawing Room to the stairs which we may ascend to the first half landing, where our progress is stopped by a barrier. On the floors above are the curatorial offices.

In a recess at the foot of the first flight is a plaster bust of William Pitt by J Flaxman (*c*.1812; related to the Glasgow statue, see pp.41 and 78). Further up is a painting by George Jones, 'The Royal Procession at the Opening of London Bridge, 1831' (commissioned by Soane and exhib. RA 1832). Among the figures are those of Soane himself, of Mrs Conduitt (who looked after Soane's household and became first Inspectress of the Museum), Chantrey and Turner (key at foot of picture). Above this picture (from left to right): King Lear, etching by J H Mortimer, 1776; Self-Portrait in Character, J H Mortimer, engraving by Robert Blyth, 1782; Caliban, etching by J H Mortimer, 1775; Ophelia, etching by J H Mortimer, 1776; Shylock, etching by J H Mortimer, 1776. John Hamilton Mortimer issued twelve etchings of Shakespearian Characters, after his own original drawings, in two sets of six in 1775 and 1776. Soane owned copies of all twelve. In the 1830 *Description* Soane described this group of five prints as '*beautiful specimens of the taste and discrimination of that great artist. Mr Mortimer gave these impressions to his friend Mr Levick; at whose death they became the property of his niece, from whom I received them*'. Miss Levick was, like Mrs Soane, a niece of George Wyatt, the builder. Also on this wall are five chalk studies of heads

Fig. 53: 'The Royal Procession at
the Opening of London Bridge'
by George Jones, 1831. Soane and
his housekeeper, Mrs Conduitt,
are in the front row either side
of the staff in the hand of the
cloaked figure (left foreground)
*Photograph: Prudence Cuming
Associates*

by Mortimer, a mezzotint by Valentine Green of a self-portrait by Mortimer, published in 1779 and two medallion portraits by Flaxman of himself and Mrs Flaxman (see also p.66), presented to Soane by Maria Denman.

Just beyond the barrier across the staircase, on the left a small door leads into what was, in Soane's day, the Tivoli Recess. This, like the Shakespeare Recess directly below, contained works of art including, on the end wall, a cast of the entablature of the Temple of Vesta. It had a painted ceiling, similar to that in the Shakespeare Recess, and an elaborate stained glass window by William Collins depicting the figure of Charity (based on a window designed by Joshua Reynolds in New College Chapel, Oxford). When the Recess was converted into a lavatory in 1917 a new window was made at the back of the Shakespeare Recess to receive the Charity window which was later bricked up again after Collins's glass was destroyed by blast damage in 1940.

Looking up at the round-headed window on the staircase, one can just see glass of a deep red colour. In the window niche is a plaster bust of Palladio.

THE SECOND FLOOR

The Museum's offices on the second floor occupy rooms that were originally the bedchambers of Sir John Soane and his wife, together with a bathroom and a watercloset, and a small boudoir which Mrs Soane called her 'morning room'. Here Eliza Soane could read or write letters surrounded by a selection of her favourite paintings and engravings. Although Soane added to the hang after her death, the inventory records made at the time of his death in 1837 record much of her arrangement which included the series of engravings of Shakespearian characters by John Hamilton Mortimer (inherited from her cousin, Miss Levick; see p.82), a watercolour of the 'Refectory at Kirkstall Abbey' by J M W Turner (see p. 32) and portraits of her mother-in-law and her eldest son, John Soane jun., by John Downman (see p.65) along with other sketches of her husband and sons.

After Mrs Soane's death, her bedchamber (the large front room on the second floor) seems to have been preserved by her husband until 1834, when he converted it into a new Model Room. These rooms were turned into a 'Curator's Apartment' after Soane's death and, until the end of World War II, the Curator was expected to live at the Museum.

As part of the plans embodied in the Museum's Masterplan (2007) it is proposed to re-instate all these rooms and open them to the public for the first time since Soane's death.

Fig. 54:
The Tivoli Recess in *c*.1834–35, watercolour by
C J Richardson
The British Library

THE MODEL ROOM

At present Soane's collection of models is displayed on the second floor of No. 12, pending the restoration of the original Model Room. Please enquire at the front door if you wish to see the models.

Soane used models extensively in his own architectural practice and also began buying additional models as works of art as early as 1804 when he purchased cork models of the Temple of Vesta at Tivoli (p.63) and the Arch of Constantine (p.66). He placed models throughout his house in both the domestic rooms at the front and the Museum at the back. However there was no room entirely devoted to models until after Soane's acquisition of a cork model of Pompeii for which he commissioned a mahogany stand with brass pillars in 1826 from Messrs Johnston, Brookes & Co. This model stand was initially placed in the South Drawing Room and then in the Basement Ante-Room until, in 1828, Soane created his first dedicated Model Room in the front attic of No. 13 (3rd floor). By 1835 the model stand had been moved again, to what had formerly been Mrs Soane's bedchamber, the front room on the second floor of No. 13 (now the Director's office) where it formed the centrepiece of a more elaborate model room. After Soane's death the models were distributed throughout the house.

The central feature of the model display is Soane's model stand of 1826, originally 9ft-square but cut down by James Wild at the end of the 19th century. Its

Fig. 55:
The Model Room
in c.1834–35,
watercolour by
C J Richardson

Fig. 56:
The rear bedroom
on the second
floor, 1825,
watercolour view

base contains deep drawers which in Soane's day held his collection of drawings
by other celebrated architects, such as Sir William Chambers, William Kent and
James Wyatt. This placed the work of these architects alongside Soane's works
in the form of the models of his own designs. Thus the model room was a sort
of miniature architectural museum in its own right. In the centre of the stand is
a large cork model of the excavations at Pompeii as they were in 1820, said (by
George Bailey, the first Curator) to have been made from measurements taken by
G L Taylor and Edward Cresy, architects who were travelling in Italy 1818–21. John
Soane junior wrote of them to his father from Rome in 1819, 'they measured
everything – Greek, Roman and Gothic'. However, the Pompeii model was made
by Domenico Padiglione, a model-maker at the Naples Museum, and he is
unlikely to have used other people's measurements since he was himself autho-
rised to measure at Pompeii. He produced a large master-model of Pompeii (now
lost) of which the Soane version is a copy to a reduced scale. Another version of it
survives in Germany. The model seems to have come to Soane from the estate of
John Sanders (d.1826) his first pupil, who travelled with Taylor and Cresy but who
probably purchased the model from Signor Gargiulo, a Naples dealer who often
negotiated sales for Padiglione. Sanders probably also owned the three large cork
models of the Doric temples at Paestum, also made by Padiglione, which are
displayed above the Pompeii model on the upper level of the model stand (see
Fig.59, p.89). They show the temples after they were tidied up in 1802. Soane had
visited both Pompeii and Paestum during his time in Italy as a student 1778–80.

Fig. 57:
The Bathroom
in 1825, water-
colour view

Also on the upper level of the central stand are ten white plaster of Paris models – reconstructions of ancient buildings – made by the Parisian model-maker François Fouquet who worked with his father, Jean-Pierre Fouquet, making models for architects and collectors (see also p.79). These include models of the Erechtheion and Tower of the Winds in Athens, the Temple of Vesta at Tivoli and the Mausoleum at Halicarnassus – one of the seven wonders of the ancient world. Soane bought 20 Fouquet models from Edward Cresy in 1834 for £100. At the west end of the model stand are three more cork models: the tomb of the Horatii and Curiati; three columns in the Campo Vaccino at Rome (supposed to be the remains of the Temple of Castor and Pollux); and the Ruins of the Temple of Jupiter Tonans (the Temple of Vespasian), Rome. Also on the upper level are three plaster models of pedestals for the Pitt Cenotaph in the National Debt Redemption Office, c.1818. Below, at the west end of the Pompeii model, is a small circular wooden model of the Castello d'Acqua (or water house) erected by Soane for Lord Hardwicke at Wimpole Hall, 1794. This model is hinged and the sections coloured pink. Soane was probably the first architect to transfer this convention from drawings to models.

Around the edge of the room are modern model stands designed by Murray John, RIBA, and made by John Graves. They are based on the proportions of the central stand and hold mostly models of Soane's own works. Soane advocated the use of models strongly in his Royal Academy Lectures, saying, 'in my own work I have seldom failed to have a model of the work proposed . . . I must add that

Fig. 58:
Model of Tyringham House,
Buckinghamshire, made
by Joseph Parkins 1793–94
Photograph: Ole Woldbye

wherever the model has been dispensed with, I am afraid the building has suffered in consequence thereof, either in solidity or convenience, and perhaps both'. He was unique among English architects between the 1780s and 1830s in using models so extensively. Over 100 models for his works survive at the Museum and many more were produced for his clients. In Soane's day more of the models of his own buildings were displayed on the central stand, alongside those of celebrated Greek and Roman buildings. Many were kept in glass cases and one bill survives stipulating yellow glass for a model case. Soane used several different model-makers and spent considerable sums – one model cost as much as £90. He also paid for inscriptions to be written on his models.

South (window) wall

Left-hand stand, upper shelf: three models for the Pitt Cenotaph in the National Debt Redemption Office, 1818. The largest shows the final design and was proba-bly for presentation before a Committee. Model of the Old Colonial or 5% Office at the Bank of England. Lower shelf: large model of Soane's Classical first design for the new Law Courts at Westminster, *c.*1823, made after he was instructed to demolish the partly-erected building and redesign the whole thing in a Gothic style. Above this stand is a perspective view of the Pitt Cenotaph by J M Gandy.

Right-hand stand, upper shelf and below, left: two models for a country villa at Acton designed by Soane for himself in 1800 but never built because Pitzhanger Manor came on to the market and was acquired instead. Upper shelf, right: Tyringham House, Buckinghamshire. This model divides horizontally into

Fig. 59: Cork model of the Temple of Neptune at Paestum, made in Naples by Domenico Padiglione
after 1802 *Photograph: Geremy Butler*

several layers to show the interiors. It is a fine example of a client model, made
for the banker William Praed in the 1790s, and was therefore never part of the
original Model Room, although it is shown in a Gandy watercolour now in the
Picture Room (p.33). It was presented to the Museum in 1918 by F A König. Below
this model, on the lower shelf, is a model of the Governor's Court at the Bank of
England, 1803–04. On the wall above are two perspective views by J M Gandy –
the interior of the mausoleum at Dulwich Picture Gallery and Tyringham House.
West wall
Left-hand stand, top shelf: model of the Privy Council and Board of Trade Offices,
Whitehall. This model shows the first *approved* design and cost £50 in 1824.
Middle shelf: mahogany model showing the masonry construction of a niche in
the Rotunda at the Bank of England, made in 1794 by Henry Provis 'for the use of
workmen'. This model was also exhibited by Soane during his Royal Academy
Lectures to illustrate the use of incombustible materials. Plaster model of the
Pantheon, Rome, by François Fouquet, 1824. Lower shelf: two models for the Law
Courts at Westminster, on the right an early version of the Gothic scheme forced
on Soane and on the left a more elaborate Gothic version, almost as executed. On
the wall above the stand is a design model showing the spacing of four columns
on the Threadneedle Street façade of the Bank of England.

On the wall, to the left of the mirror: various small models for ceilings and
lantern lights at the Law Courts and, below these, a model showing a truss girder
and floor joists at the Bank of England, 1816.

On the mantel-shelf: No. 13 Lincoln's Inn Fields façade, 1812. This model was
made for use as part of Soane's evidence at the court case in 1812 over the

projecting loggia on the front of the house, which was alleged by the District Surveyor to be in breach of the building regulations. Cork model showing the relative proportions of columns at Paestum. Unidentified model, possibly for windows in the Royal Gallery, Westminster, 1823.

On the stand in front of the fireplace: a cork model of the Temple of Neptune, Paestum, attributed to Augusto Rosa. This shows the temple prior to the clearing-out of 1802 and was in Soane's possession by 1817.

On the wall, to the right of the mirror: model showing three bays on the Downing Street façade of the Privy Council and Board of Trade Offices, 1828. Model of part of the Prince's Street façade, Bank of England. Model of plaster spandril from the Masonic Hall, Freemasons' Tavern, Great Queen Street, 1828.

Right-hand stand, top: model of the central portion of the Threadneedle Street façade, Bank of England and, in front, two models showing the development of building from the Primitive Hut, made to illustrate Soane's first RA Lecture (delivered in 1809). The right-hand model is the more primitive and also less finished model. Middle shelf: two models for the Simeon Monument, Reading, 1804. Plaster model by Fouquet of the Temple of Venus at Baalbec. Model of a preliminary design for Holy Trinity Church, St Marleybone, 1822, made for the Church Commissioners and showing two alternative nave elevations. Bottom shelf: plaster model by Fouquet of a monument at Palmyra. Wooden model made to show the interior of the £5 Note Office (Public Drawing Office) at the Bank of England, 1803. The viewer is intended to look at the interior through the open east end.

North Wall

Far left, on the wall: plan model of the Law Courts made in 1827 to accompany Soane's pamphlet *A brief statement of the proceedings respecting the New Law Courts* (1828). Model of the Lothbury façade of the Bank of England, 1800.

Model stand, left of doors, upper shelf: two plaster models for the Tivoli Corner at the north-west angle of the Bank of England, 1804 (inspired by the Temple of Vesta at Tivoli, one of the buildings Soane most admired). The left-hand model shows an intermediate design and the one on the right is as executed. In front of the models are three designs for the Bosanquet tomb in St Mary's Churchyard, Leytonstone (demolished 1960s) designed in 1806 after the death of Samuel Bosanquet, a director of the Bank. These models may have inspired Giles Gilbert Scott, (who became Chairman of the Trustees of the Soane Museum in 1925), when he was designing the 'K2' red telephone box in 1924–26, with its Soanic shallow dome and incised mouldings flush with the surface. Lower shelf: two models for the Bank of England, on the left Lothbury Court, 1799, and on the right the Bullion Gateway, 1796.

Above the doors: model of the eastern end of the Threadneedle Street façade of the Bank of England.

Between the doors: a study model of the corner of the New State Paper Office, Duke Street and St James's Park, Westminster, 1830–31. Soane used this model to experiment with different forms of rustication – vermiculated on the basement and banded above.

Right of doors, on the wall: model of an unidentified ceiling. A sectional plan model of the Court of King's Bench, 1828, made for the authorities before work began. Soane seems to have been unique in producing sectional plan models. Two examples of the hollow terracotta bricks used by Soane in the construction of the vaulted ceilings at the Bank of England. They were produced by a kiln set up on the site. There are more examples on the floor in front of the fireplace.

On the model stand, upper shelf: model of the Houses of Parliament showing the routes into the two chambers from the new Members' Entrance built in 1833 on St Margaret's Street. Lower shelf: sectional plan model for the Court of Common Pleas, 1822–23, probably made for the authorities before the court was built.

On the corner stand to the right: a model of the north-west angle of the New State Paper Office, 1830–31, which shows Soane experimenting with the decoration of the façade and the treatment of the windows.

East wall

Over the door: model of part of the new roof of the Banqueting House, Whitehall, executed by Soane 1829. As Attached Architect to the Office of Works, Soane was responsible for the fabric of the Banqueting House and, after a survey in 1828, found it necessary to construct an entirely new roof. This model was not only a design exercise but was used by Soane to show the carpenters exactly what he wanted.

On the wall above the fireplace (left): five models of roof trusses. The top one shows George Dance's design for trussed girders which he sent to Soane on request in 1802.

Above the fireplace is a perspective view by J M Gandy of the Scala Regia, the entrance to the House of Lords, designed by Soane 1822–23.

On the mantel-shelf: two models showing a method of constructing groined arches with bricks devised by George Tappen, *c.*1808. A model of the central bay of the attic on the Lothbury façade at the Bank.

On the model stand to the left of the fireplace: a plaster model of the New State Paper Office, 1830s. It does not show the whole of the building and, unusually, the omitted section of the building is illustrated by a watercolour perspective attached to the back of the model. Below this model is one for the bridge at Tyringham, 1790s.

On the model stand to the right of the fireplace, which is one of Soane's own, is a model showing the Bank Stock Office, as executed, made by Joseph Parkin. Parkin spent 22 days in February and March 1793 making this model and was paid £8 11s 4d. An Account Book entry in May 1792 shows Soane's coppersmith Samuel Rehe being paid £18 for a model of the Bank Stock Office roof in brass and fretwork, probably that used in Parkin's model. The Bank Stock Office was re-created in the 1980s and forms part of the Bank of England Museum (see p.148).

NO. 14 LINCOLN'S INN FIELDS

Soane purchased No. 14 on 14 October 1823, when he was 70, for £1,480 from Abel Moysey. His incentive was perhaps in part a wish to create a symmetrical group of buildings in the centre of the north side of Lincoln's Inn Fields. This had been in his mind as early as 1812–13 when he prepared drawings for an extended façade for Nos 13–15. Another pressing need was to extend his 'Museum' at the back of No. 13. He had recently purchased the four large paintings of Hogarth's 'An Election' series (see p.26) and the opportunity to build a new Picture Room at the back of No. 14 offered an immediate solution to the problem of where to hang them.

From the start Soane intended to demolish and re-build the whole of No. 14. He began with the part he intended to keep for his own use, at the back of the site (the courtyard and the stable block beyond). By 17 November 1823 this area had been cleared (leaving the main No. 14 house untouched) and Soane then began its re-construction, creating the Picture Room, Museum Corridor, Monk's Parlour and Monk's Yard. The re-building of the main house did not start until after this new extension to his Museum was completed in about April 1824.

In June 1824 the building materials from the No. 14 main house were offered for sale at auction in lots to be taken down and cleared away by the purchasers (as had happened previously for the rear premises). In July Soane began work on the designs but work on site did not begin until May 1825. Five months later, in October 1825, the top mansard was being slated but some building work continued until the end of 1826 (the glazier was paid in that year) with small elements of interior work continuing into 1827.

The construction of No. 14 was carried out by craftsmen well known to Soane, many of whom had worked on Nos 12 and 13, such as the Martyr family (carpenters and joiners), the mason Thomas Grundy, plumber William Good, painter and glazier William Watson and smith Thomas Russell. Mrs Sarah Yandall provided rubbish carting and night watchman services.

Soane intended to lease the house to tenants, complete except for 'bell hanging, papering' and the top coat of paint, with a covenant to ensure that the house was occupied by a family and not sub-let as commercial premises. In June 1828 the first tenants, Messrs Williams and Bethell, moved in; their lease required them to complete the decorations 'in a very superior manner'. A two-year dispute with Soane then followed in which Soane contended that he had been duped as the house was being used as commercial Chambers whereas he had understood it was to be lived in by a family. He further objected to unauthorised alterations to the ground floor made in the interim and the non-completion of the decoration of the house. The dispute was eventually resolved and Williams and Bethell remained Soane's tenants until his death.

On Soane's death in 1837 No. 14 was included with the personal estate not forming the endowment of the Museum and passed into Chancery in a dispute over his Will. It was finally sold in 1874 after the abolition of the Court of Chancery. The freehold has changed hands a number of times. It came up for sale in 1962 when Sir John Summerson, the then Curator, applied to the Treasury for a grant to purchase it for the Museum. His application was turned down and the freehold was acquired by the Equity and Law Life Assurance Society Ltd. In 1996 the freehold was offered for sale again and was acquired for the Museum with the help of grants from the Heritage Lottery Fund and other Trusts and Foundations through Sir John Soane's Museum Society. The house had tenants and it was therefore not until May 2006 that its restoration could begin on site.

The Museum's Research Library will move into two floors of the building at the end of 2007 and a new Children's Education Centre will open in the basement.

APPENDIX I

CHRONOLOGY OF SIR JOHN SOANE'S MUSEUM

1753 John Soan born 10 September, youngest child of John Soan, bricklayer, of Goring-on-Thames, near Reading.

1768 Introduced to James Peacock and, through him, entered the office of George Dance the Younger (1741–1825).

1771 Admitted to the Royal Academy Schools, 25 October as a student of architecture.

1772 Appointed to a junior post in the office of Henry Holland (1745–1806) at a salary of £60 per annum. Won Royal Academy Silver Medal for measured drawing of Whitehall Banqueting House, December. Exhibited for the first time at the Royal Academy.

1774 Unsuccessfully competed for Royal Academy Gold Medal.

1776 Won Royal Academy Gold Medal (subject, a Triumphal Bridge) in December. Medal presented by Sir Joshua Reynolds.

1777 Living at 7 Hamilton Street, Piccadilly, by March. Triumphal Bridge designs submitted by Sir William Chambers to George III, who expressed his approbation. General Assembly of the Royal Academy voted to recommend to the King that Soane be appointed travelling student to Italy for three years, December.

1778 Soane published *Designs in Architecture*. Left for Italy in the company of Robert Brettingham (*c.*1750–1806), 18 March. In Paris met Jean-Rodolphe Perronet, civil engineer. Arrived Rome 2 May. Met Frederick Hervey, Bishop of Derry, September or October. Met Piranesi, probably by letter of introduction from Sir William Chambers, before 9 November and was given four engravings of Piranesi's work. Met Thomas Pitt, probably around December. Travelled to Naples with the Bishop of Derry, 22–29 December.

1779 Returned to Rome with the Bishop of Derry, 12–14 March. Travelled to Naples with Rowland Burdon, John Patteson and others, 11–14 April. Set sail for Sicily 21 April, reaching Palermo 28 April. Crossed from Sicily to Malta about the last week in May, returning 2 June. Arrived back in Naples 1 or 2 July and departed for Rome. Back in Rome by 19 July. Travelled to Venice with Rowland Burdon via Bologna, Parma, Milan, Verona, Vicenza and Padua, beginning of August. Returned to Rome via Florence, October.

1780 Invited to become the Earl of Bristol's architect at Downhill, January, Frederick Hervey, Bishop of Derry, having succeeded to the title of 4th Earl of Bristol, 23

December 1779. Elected to the Accademia del Disegno, Florence, 10 January. Made plans for John Stuart for Allanbank, Scotland, April. Obtained passport to return to England by way of France, and left Rome with the Revd George Holgate and his pupil, Mr Pepper, 19 April. Arrived in Florence 23 April. Probably met the young singer Anna Storace then performing at the Teatro dell Pergola. New passport issued to return to England via Germany. Left Florence 28 April. Travelled via Bologna, 30 April; Padua, 2 May; Vicenza, 3 May; Verona, 4 May; Mantua, 8 May; Parma, 9 May; and Milan, 10 May. Left Milan for Genoa 12 May, arriving 14 May. Returned to Milan 19–21 May. Travelled to Como for the overnight crossing, 22 May. Arrived in Chivenna 23 May and stayed one and a half days while awaiting transport over the Alps. 'Passed the Mountains to Tusano' (Thusis) and continued to 'Coira' (Chur), 26 May. Drew the wooden bridges at Reichenau for the Earl of Bristol. Obtained a letter of safe conduct 27 May, and travelled by coach to Walendstadt and thence by boat to Wessen and Zurich. Left Zurich 30 May for Shauffhausen via Wettingen, making studies of the bridges in both places. Travelled to Basel, 1 June, probably on this leg of the journey losing his Royal Academy medals, some books, drawing instruments, drawings and letters from his trunk on the road. Travelled to Freiburg, 7 June; Keyl, 8 June; Cologne, 15 June; Liege, 16 June; Louvain and Brussels, 18 June. From thence he probably travelled to Ostend and made the Channel crossing some time in the last 10 days of June. Then to Ireland, arriving at Downhill, 27 July. Left on 2 September, the commission having been cancelled. In Scotland and County Durham on various commissions, September to October. Returned to London and rented rooms in 10 Cavendish Street, November.

1781 Elected to Honorary Membership of the Parma Academy, 13 March. Rented the first floor and the front room on the second floor at 53 Margaret Street, Cavendish Square, June. Commenced practice in London.

1784 Married Elizabeth (Eliza) Smith, niece of George Wyatt, a wealthy builder, 21 August. Began to spell his name Soane. Took his first pupil, John Sanders, for 5 years from 1 September.

1786 John Soane, junior, born, 29 April. Moved to 77 Welbeck Street, of which he had purchased the lease, 30 November. This remained his home until he moved to No. 12 Lincoln's Inn Fields in 1794.

1787 Soane bought materials from the demolition of Wricklemarsh House at Blackheath and may have acquired his set of Chinese chairs, bearing the arms of its owner Sir Gregory Page (see p.8), in the same year.

1788 Appointed architect to the Bank of England. Published *Plans. . . of Buildings erected in the counties of Norfolk, Suffolk &c.*

1789 George Soane born, 28 September.

1790 Mrs Soane's uncle Wyatt died, leaving her a considerable sum of money in the form of property, 23 February. Soane established a separate office at Albion Place, Blackfriars, in property inherited from Wyatt. Soane appointed Clerk of Works to St James's Palace, the Houses of Parliament and other public buildings in Westminster, October (resigned 1793). The first recorded purchase of works of art by Soane is a payment, in this year, to Flaxman of £1 10s 'for two lions' and 5 gns for 'two pairs of vases', The lions were probably plaster models of the antique bronze examples at Florence, one of which survives in the Museum. The vases were probably Wedgwood 'Etruscan' ware, of which one pair and another single specimen survive.

1791 Soane moved his office to Great Scotland Yard, Whitehall, in April. This remained his office until the move to No. 12 Lincoln's Inn Fields in 1794.

1792 No. 12 Lincoln's Inn Fields purchased in June and Soane began demolition immediately prior to complete rebuilding for his own occupation. He and his family moved in in 1794. This house, next door westwards from No. 13, officially became part of the Museum in 1971. The freehold formed part of the original endowment of the Museum. A drawing of the ground-floor back parlour in 1798 suggests that Soane at this period had collected little except books. Two lions (probably the pair bought from Flaxman in 1790) and two models of antique statues stand on the bookcases and there are two Wedgwood 'Etruscan' vases (possibly one of the two pairs bought from Flaxman). The pictures include Soane's Silver Medal drawing of the Banqueting House and a number of Piranesi engravings, which he acquired in Italy. In this year, Soane paid Benjamin Grant a total of £21 19s for casts.

1793 Soane published *Sketches in Architecture*. Soane paid Nathaniel Marchant 'for the remainder of the subscription to a set of impressions from gems (see p.15) £2 2s'. Soane drew up a catalogue of his books.

1794 Soane and his family moved into No. 12 Lincoln's Inn Fields and slept their first night there on 18 January. Soane's office was also transferred to Lincoln's Inn Fields.

1795 Soane elected an Associate of the Royal Academy and a Fellow of the Society of Antiquaries. He was appointed Deputy Surveyor of His Majesty's Woods and Forests (resigned 1799). Soane paid £40 10s for casts at the sale of the Scottish architect James Playfair's effects.

1796 Soane bought from his friend E Foxhall, for 5 gns two small drawings by John

Webber (p.31) and purchased at Christie's 8 coloured prints of frescoes found in the grounds of the Villa Negroni (p.71). Soane made his first purchase of oil paintings at the Highcliffe sale of the Earl of Bute's collection at Christie's when Mrs Soane bid on his behalf for two Canalettos (see p.64).

1797 Soane purchased at Christie's a drawing by Clérisseau of a mausoleum (£15 15s).

1798 Soane paid John Downman 20 gns for portraits of his mother and of his son, John. He also bought for 12 gns at Christie's, a drawing by George Barret (p.31). Also more casts from Benjamin Grant (£4 9s). Soane became a Magistrate and paid for a certificate for armorial bearings (16 July).

1799 Soane purchased a fine copy of Sir William Hamilton's *Campi Phlegraei* from the bookseller Mr Faulder for £20.

1800 Pitzhanger Manor, Ealing, acquired by Soane and rebuilt by him (1800–02) as a country retreat and with an eye to the artistic education of his two sons. The house still exists, has been restored and is now open to the public (see p.148). This enterprise stimulated Soane to collect in a more ambitious way and the beginnings of the Soane Museum may be said to date from these years. At Christie's, in 1800, he bought a landscape by Zuccarelli in oils (p.31) for £15 4s 6d. At the Cawdor sale at Christie's he bought three antique vases, including the large krater known as 'the Cawdor vase' (p.9). These, with the coach-hire, cost him £80 8s 6d. At the Dr Stevens sale, again at Christie's, he paid £43 7s for four Clérisseaus and a coloured drawing of the Aldobrandini Marriage.

1801 Soane made his first considerable purchase of antique marbles at the sale, by Christie's, of the Earl of Bessborough's collection at Roehampton. The main items were six cinerary urns, the Ephesian Diana and statue of Aesculapius (p.55) and an altar, and the total price £212. These, with the vases bought in the previous year, were installed at Pitzhanger, the front and back parlours being specially designed to receive them. He bought another urn, a vase and other objects (total £74 19s) at the Duke of St Alban's sale. He also increased his collection of casts by purchases of architectural specimens at the Willey Reveley sale (£21) and a crouching Venus (p.46) at the Romney sale.

1802 Soane was elected a full Royal Academician 10 February and to the Vestry of the Parish of St Giles-in-the-Fields, 11 February. A year of important purchases, all destined for Pitzhanger. In February, Mrs Soane bid at Christie's for Hogarth's *A Rake's Progress* (p.22), securing the eight canvases for £570. Soane paid 40 gns to Mr C Hunter for Watteau's *L'Accordée du Village* (p.34) and at the James Clark sale at Christie's bought 40 antique vases and a bronze (total £38 14s 6d). These vases, with those already purchased, form the bulk of the collection of vases now in the Museum. At the Lord Mendip sale seven more cinerary urns, some marble vases, etc., were acquired (total £85 19s). Other purchases during the year included a Fuseli painting from Henry Tresham (p.30, Fig. 14) and from Edward Burch a head of Inigo Jones (p.12) and casts from gems (p.15) (£25 4s).

1804 Soane had his portrait painted by William Owen (25 gns) (p.76). Mrs Soane bought two watercolours from J M W Turner (pp.32 & 35). Purchases included cork models of the Arch of Constantine and Temple of Vesta at Tivoli, (pp.63 & 66) and a cinerary urn with a sphinx, all from John Govan's sale at Phillips (£65 8s 6d). Soane also acquired some Piranesi engravings from Mr Colville.

1805 Owen painted the double portrait of John and George Soane (50 gns, p.76). Purchases included 10 more drawings by Clérisseau (100 gns, from Dr Monro) and two paintings, William Hamilton's *Richard II* (p.30), and the large *Merry Wives of Windsor* by Durno, from the sale at Christie's of the contents of Boydell's Shakespeare Gallery (p.73).

1806 Soane elected Professor of Architecture at the Royal Academy on 28 March. Another drawing by Clérisseau (7 gns) and two other drawings were bought at the Lord Lansdowne sale.

1807 Appointed Clerk of Works to Chelsea Hospital, 2 March. Soane bought for 150 gns the Canaletto view of the *Riva degli Schiavoni* (p.62) at the sale of the contents of Fonthill Splendens. He appears to have hung it in his official residence at Chelsea Hospital. At the same sale he purchased a *View of Choultry, near Rajahpore,* by Hodges. In the summer of this year, Soane began negotiating to buy the freehold of No. 13 Lincoln's Inn Fields and prepared designs for a Museum and a new office on the site of the former stables at the back. The designs included a 'model room' or 'plaster room' which, in its final form, became the present Dome. He bought some (unidentified) fragments from Mrs Bonomi for 10 gns.

1808 In early summer the sale of No. 13 to Soane was completed. Soane demolished the stable block at the back of No. 13 and began to build an extension to his office and a gallery for the display of casts at the back of No. 13.

1809 Soane delivered his first Lecture at the Royal Academy, 27 March. The Dome and new offices were completed as an annexe to No. 12. Lincoln's Inn Fields. Sundry 'statues, etc.' were bought, through a Mr Walker, from Lord Yarborough (£9 2s) whose Chelsea house Soane was about to demolish. Six paintings by Luigi Mayer were bought at the Sir Robert Ainslie sale at Christie's (£5 13s).

1810 In this year Soane disposed of Pitzhanger Manor in July. The prospect of his sons adopting his profession had begun to fade and the prime purpose of Pitzhanger, therefore, disappeared and the antiquities and works of art were brought to Lincoln's Inn Fields. The only important purchase seems to have been the John Thorpe album bought at the C F Greville sale (p.135). Soane became a Justice of the Peace for the County of Middlesex and one of the Licensing Magistrates for the Holborn Division (resigned 1836).

1811 The cast of the Apollo Belvedere, which had belonged to Lord Burlington, was installed in the Dome (p.60). Soane made several purchases at Paul Sandby's sale.

1812 No. 13 Lincoln's Inn Fields rebuilt. The Dome and the old office at the back of the No. 12 site (which had become a 'library' or 'study' between 1808 and 1812) were now separated from No. 12 and made accessible from No. 13. Some drawings and a cinerary urn and vase were bought at various sales at Christie's. Soane paid £40 for the two Coade Stone caryatids now at the top of the façade of No. 13. (p.3) Soane wrote his manuscript *Crude Hints towards a history of my house.* Soane acquired marbles, probably from Henry Holland's collection, from Holland's nephew, Henry Rowles.

1813 Mr and Mrs Soane moved into No. 13 Lincoln's Inn Fields. Soane was appointed Attached Architect to the Office of Works along with John Nash and Robert Smirke. He was also appointed Grand Superintendent of Works to the United Fraternity of Freemasons.

1814 Soane met Tsar Alexander I of Russia at the Bank of England and presented him with drawings. The Tsar gave Soane a diamond ring (handed over to the Soane family in 1837). Soane lent *A Rake's Progress* to the British Institution. Soane visited Paris, 15 August–5 September.

1815 George Soane published two anonymous articles in *The Champion,* 10 and 24 September reviling his father's architecture. The discovery of the authorship was described by Soane as 'the death-blow' to his wife. Mrs Soane died, 22 November. She lay in state in the Library. She was buried in St Giles-in-the-Fields parish burial ground at St Pancras. (A tomb was erected there to Soane's design 1816, see p.148).

1816 Probably in this year Soane acquired more of the large collection of antique fragments which had been assembled in Rome in 1794–96 by Heathcote Tatham for Henry Holland. Holland had offered the collection to the Trustees of the British Museum, who had declined. Dying in 1806, he appears to have left the collection to his nephew, Henry Rowles, from whom Soane may have purchased it. Soane was arranging the marbles in the Study in 1816, and two drawings in 1817 show them in position. Mrs Sarah (Sally) Conduitt became Soane's Housekeeper.

1817 George Dance gave Soane a book of drawings by Sir Christopher Wren (p.135).

1818 At the sale, at Christie's, of Robert Adam's library and effects, Soane made some important purchases, spending £181 18s on books and £27 16s on casts, marbles, etc. (64 casts and about 23 marbles, including marble vases) see pp.16 & 61.

1819 Soane visited Paris with William Pilkington, Mr and Mrs Conduitt and Henry Parke, 21 August–23 September. The *Pasticcio* was erected in the Monument Court (p.9). The old office (site of the present New Picture Room) was made into a picture room and here *A Rake's Progress* hung until shortly after 1824.

1820 Soane paid Mr Watts £5 5s for drawings by Sir William Chambers. Mrs Soane's dog, Fanny, died and was buried in a monument in the front yard of No. 13.

1821 Soane was elected a Fellow of the Royal Society. At the Lady Thomond sale in May, Soane bought Reynolds's *Snake in the Grass* (p.8) for 500 gns, and Reynolds's notebooks for 100 gns. At the Cosway sale at Christie's in the same month he bought a number of small terracottas, alabasters, bronzes, etc. (total £21 9s), including the Triform Diana (p.13) and the Guelfi model for the Craggs monument (p.41).

1822 Acquisitions included James Ward's posthumous portrait of Mrs Soane's pet dog, Fanny (40 gns, p.72), bronze fragments of an Arab jug from the G B Belzoni sale, a marble bust of Livy and Vasi's engraved panoramic view of Rome.

1823 Soane bought Hogarth's *Election* series (p.26), for £1,732 10s at the sale of Mrs Garrick's effects at Christie's. At the Englefield sale at Christie's he bought an important vase (£34 13s, p.6) and the Pantheon pilaster capital, which had been in the Duke of St Albans' collection (p.62). At the Nollekens sale (also at Christie's) he bought various antiquities, including three busts. On 14 October Soane purchased No. 14 Lincoln's Inn Fields from Abel Moysey for £1,480. His eldest son, John, died on 21 October and was buried in the Soane tomb (p.148).

1824 A year of important changes. Soane rebuilt No. 14 Lincoln's Inn Fields, which he had bought in the previous year, and, on the rear portion of the site, built a new Picture Room, with the Monk's Parlour below. The central courtyard became Soane's 'Monk's Yard'. Now, or shortly afterwards, he walled off the old picture-room (formerly the office) from the Museum, making it again part of No. 12. It remained thus till the present New Picture Room was built in 1889. The great acquisition this year was the 'Belzoni Sarcophagus' (p.47), for which, after the British Museum had declined it, Soane paid £2,000 to Henry Salt, Belzoni's patron.

1825 The third storey was added to No.13. The Fauntleroy (grangerized) Pennant (p.136) was bought at Sotheby's for £694 13s. At the Yarnold sale and at the Revd C A North sale Soane bought various small antiquities, Egyptian, medieval and later. On 23, 26 and 30 March this year he held receptions in honour of the acquisition of the sarcophagus (p.47). At the end of the year, Westmacott's Nymph was installed in the Picture Room Recess (p.34). Soane purchased the 'Napoleon' pistol (p.73).

1827 John Britton published *The Union of Architecture, Sculpture and Painting*, a description of Soane's house and galleries, dedicated to George IV. At Lord Berwick's sale at Attingham Park, Soane bought the Josephus MS (p.136) for 140 gns, a book of Indian miniatures (p.135) for 5 gns, a cork model of an Etruscan tomb and a bust of 'Augustus Caesar when a boy' (now identified as a copy after Polycleitos, p.61). He also acquired the Astronomical Clock (p.6) which had belonged to the Duke of York, who died in this year, and paid John Britton £19 19s for drawings by Sir William Chambers and Inigo Jones bought at Christie's. Soane commissioned Francis Danby's painting *Scene from the Merchant of Venice* (£152 10s; p.79).

1828 Soane sat to Sir Thomas Lawrence for his portrait (p.4) and to Sir Francis Chantrey for the bust (p.60) which the sculptor presented to him, both portraits being installed in the following year. John Jackson also painted him in this year along with a pendant portrait of Mrs Soane (p.30). Soane purchased a bust of Homer from J Smith. He lent Canaletto's *Riva degli Schiavoni* (p.62) for exhibition at the British Institution. Soane published *Designs for Public and Private Buildings.*

1829 Landino's *Commentario Sopra Dante* (p.137) and a MS of Tasso's *Gerusalemme Liberata* (p.136), purchased at the sale of the Earl of Guildford's library. A 13th-century Bible, (p.136) presented by Mr Herring of Norwich. The Tivoli Recess was created and the Chantrey bust of Soane placed there. An initial payment of £50 was made by Soane for William Collins's painted window of 'Charity', after one by Reynolds in the Chapel of New College, Oxford (p.83). The final payment of £95 was made in 1832, when the window was installed in the Tivoli Recess (it was destroyed in 1941). The ground floor loggia was glazed in, thus extending the Library. The Monk's Cell was created and Soane bought the Flemish carved wood Crucifixion (p.39) from W Watson for £12. The Shakespeare Recess (p.73) was created and the painting *The Vision of Shakespeare* (p.74) commissioned from Henry Howard.

1830 From about this time Soane began to commission paintings from his Academy colleagues and other artists, often paying very high prices. Already by 1827 he owned examples of the work of Turner, Fuseli, Bourgeois, Maria Cosway, Bird, Howard and Westall. Now he paid £500 to Augustus Callcott for *The Passage Point* (p.64) and 150 gns to C L Eastlake for *Una and the Red Cross Knight* (p.30). He bought the Nicholas Stone MSS (p.136) for £34 15s from a Mr Tiffen, who had obtained them at the James Paine sale, also the Cossia portrait of Napoleon (p.73). Soane loaned the Lawrence portrait of himself to the British Institution. In this year Soane published the first edition of the *Description of the Residence of John Soane, Architect,* with lithographs by C Haghe. The Lawrence portrait of Soane was engraved by Charles Turner.

1831 Soane bought Turner's *Van Tromp's Barge* (p.79) for 250 gns and Henry Howard's *Circe* for £300. Soane was knighted by William IV on 21 September after 17 years as Architect attached to the Office of Works. Soane became a member of the Garrick Club (founded 1831).

1832 Soane commissioned George Jones to paint *The Opening of London Bridge* (p.82) for 300 gns, and Henry Howard to paint *The Contention of Oberon and Titania* (p.72) for 250 gns. He purchased two paintings by W Daniell for £23 8s (p.66) and a breviary for £520 from a Mr Boone. The Officers of the Works presented the Westmacott bust of Sir William Chambers (p.44). Another edition of the *Description* was produced, with additional plates, but unchanged text. Published *Plans, Elevations and Perspective Views of Pitzhanger Manor House.*

1833 Soane retired as Architect to the Bank, at the age of 80, after 45 years. The original Dome skylight at the back of the Museum was replaced by one identical to that present today. The replacement was more restrained and less picturesque than the original, having no coloured glass. Soane bought 54 volumes of drawings by Robert and James Adam from the Adam family for £200 (p.136). The 'King Charles' jewel was bought at the Mrs Barnes sale at Redland Hall, Bristol, and sundry antiquities at the C H Tatham sale at Christie's. The Grimani commentary (p.136) and two other MSS bought from the Duke of Buckingham for £735. On 20 April of this year, the *Act for settling and preserving Sir John Soane's Museum* received the Royal Assent, see Appendix II.

1834 In this year the open loggias on the first and second floors were glazed and opened into the rooms behind them; and Henry Howard was paid £415 for the panels for the Library and Dining Room ceilings (p.10). Maria Denman was paid £20 for casts and models by her brother-in-law, John Flaxman. Soane paid

George Jones £250 for his painting of *The Smoking House at Chelsea Hospital.* Hilton's *Marc Antony* was commissioned at 100 gns, and the 20 plaster models of antique buildings by François Fouquet were acquired from Edward Cresy for £100. Lewis Wyatt was paid 50 gns for his collection of some 90 casts (procured by him in Rome in 1820), and Messrs Rundell and Bridge presented a cast of the Shield of Achilles. Soane purchased a collection of Peruvian vases for £6 (p.39). Soane purchased from the Duke of Buckingham a large collection of antique gems, for which he paid £1,000.

1835 Soane was presented with a Gold Medal by the Architects of England, paid for by 350 subscribers and modelled by W Wyon from the Chantrey bust (p.60). The medal was privately presented at No. 13 Lincoln's Inn Fields on 24 March. Soane was apparently too moved to reply to the Address read out to him. At Freemasons' Hall in the evening silver and bronze reproductions of the Soane Medal were presented to the subscribers. The Chantrey bust (lent by Soane for the occasion) was placed on a pedestal with a banner above it inscribed in gold letters, 'Soane Festival'. The hall was decorated with flowers, busts of Vitruvius, Palladio, Michelangelo, Inigo Jones, Wren and Adam and drawings of Soane designs. A Ball concluded the evening's festivities. Pictures acquired this year included Wheatley and Mortimer's *View in the Privy Gardens, Whitehall,* Mrs Pope's *Flowers of Shakespeare* (30 gns,) and Lebelle's paintings on silk (p.72). Benjamin L Vulliamy was paid £43 14s for the clock now in the Breakfast Room. In this year Soane was engaged on a revised *Description,* with new illustrations, of which 150 copies were printed and privately circulated. His *Memoirs of the Professional Life of an Architect* was also privately published. George Bailey began the Inventory of the Works of Art and Pictures in the Museum. The first Visitors' Book for No. 13 Lincoln's Inn Fields dates from this year.

1836 The Dance drawings (in the Dance Cabinet) purchased from the architect's son, Sir Charles Dance, for £500 (p.79). In November of this year Soane sealed up a number of drawers, cupboards and other repositories containing his correspondence, miscellaneous papers and objects, leaving inscriptions with the dates on which each was to be opened (see the years 1866, 1886 and 1896).

1837 Sir John Soane died on 20 January, probably in the second-floor back room which, at that date, was subdivided into a small bedroom, with bathroom, oratory and lobby adjoining. The first meeting of the Trustees appointed under the Act was held on 6 February with George Bailey, Soane's chief clerk, attending as Curator, appointed under Soane's Will. The public were admitted by ticket on certain days from 4 April, about 64 visitors attending each day.

Some of Soane's furniture was (most improperly) sold and a large round table purchased (£20) for Trustees' meetings. These were held monthly. Bailey completed the Inventory of the Museum's contents and numbered each work of art. The Henry Howard painting from the Library ceiling '*Phoebus in his car, preceded by Aurora and the Morning Star*' was lent to the Royal Academy Exhibition in April. Soane had agreed this loan before his death and the painting had only been temporarily fixed to allow for this. Under Soane's Will the main house at No. 14 Lincoln's Inn Fields (rented out since it was completed in 1826) was included with his personal estate not forming part of the endowment of the Museum. Along with the rest of the personal estate it passed into Chancery in the case of Conduitt versus Soane and others, a dispute about Soane's Will. The Court of Chancery was abolished in 1873 and No. 14 finally sold in 1874.

1838 Soane's relatives petitioned the House of Commons for the removal of the Museum and the division among them of the Trust funds. The Trustees successfully counter-petitioned. The Dance Cabinet was moved from the Library to the Monk's Parlour.

1839 The stonework of the exterior of the house painted. It remained so till 1937.

1840 George Bailey's *Handbook* published.

1841 J Seguier employed to clean and varnish 45 paintings, i.e. nearly all except those by Turner and Jones.

1843 Library catalogue printed.

1844 HRH Prince Albert became a Trustee (representing the Royal Society of Arts). He remained on the Board until 1856. The ceilings of the Library and Breakfast Room were cleaned, the paint and varnish, gilding and bronzing were touched up.

1847 Soane's grandson, John Soane, requested permission to reside in the Museum in accordance with a provision in the Act of 1833. He died in Madeira in the following year while his position was being considered by the Trustees.

1848 Seguier cleaned the paintings not dealt with in 1841.

1849 The metal gratings used by Soane in the Dome area, Museum South Passage and Corridor to admit light to the basement were removed and 'rough plate glass' installed in the apertures. The eight paintings of Hogarth's 'A Rake's Progress' were removed from the Picture Room (where they hung behind the north planes) and hung on screens in the South Drawing Room.

1850 The Pompeian Model stand was removed from Soane's Model Room (front room 2nd floor) to the north part of the Library on the ground floor. The volume of Wren drawings for Hampton Court Palace was rebound by Tuckett, the bookbinder to the British Museum and the drawings remounted. The collection of Dodwell and Vespignani drawings were arranged and mounted in large albums (now Vols 22–24).

1851 The year of the Great Exhibition. The Trustees therefore opened the Museum on additional days, being open Monday, Tuesday, Thursday and Friday from May to September in addition to the usual days in February–April. The Museum was open on 108 days, with an average attendance of 77 visitors per day. Total visitor numbers were 7,357.

1851 Thick glass panels substituted for three wooden panels in the upper part of the front door to admit more light into the front Hall.

1853 Owen Jones, on behalf of the Crystal Palace Company, applied to make a cast of the Seti Sarcophagus for the Crystal Palace; this was eventually refused.

1854 The walls of the Staircase were re-marbled and varnished and the woodwork grained in 'wainscot'.

1855 A new copper roof over the main building (i.e. to the third floor of No. 13) was ordered.

1857 A fire hose laid on from the cistern at the top of the house and leather fire buckets placed in the Museum.

1858 The Trustees decided to advertise the Museum's opening hours in various papers, beginning with *The Times* once a week.

1859 The Breakfast Parlour repainted, varnished and gilded.

1860 On the motion of Mr J T Platt, the House of Commons ordered an enquiry into the administration and accessibility of the Museum. A report was submitted by the Trustees and no further action was taken. George Soane, the architect's younger son, died aged 71 on 12 July. In December both George Bailey, the Curator, and Mrs Conduitt, the Inspectress, died.

1861 Joseph Bonomi appointed Curator; Miss Elizabeth Harris, Inspectress. Bonomi's election was not confirmed for two years, owing to some doubt about his qualification as an architect. The Museum opened on 18 April and was open on only 30 days with 1,354 visitors.

1862 The 12 Hogarth paintings were lent to the International Exhibition at South Kensington, parliamentary powers having been obtained for this purpose. The Trustees decided to open the Museum Wednesday, Thursday and Friday from April to August (longer than usual because of the International Exhibition). Henry Howard's 'Oberon and Titania', Bourgeois's 'Kemble as Coriolanus' and

Watteau's 'LAccordée du Village' were 'cleaned and restored' by a Mr Smart. The Turner oil 'Admiral van Tromp's barge' and the Watteau were glazed.

1863 The twelve Hogarth paintings were glazed. Bonomi pieced together the fragments of the sarcophagus lid, setting them in plaster of Paris, and had wooden frames made for them.

1865 The interior of the Museum repainted, the sarcophagus cleaned and given a coat of shellac.

1866 The sarcophagus enclosed in a glass case. The Trustees opposed a proposal for an underground railway, passing under Lincoln's Inn Fields. Certain drawers and a cupboard, sealed by Sir John Soane with instructions that they should not be opened until 22 November 1866, were inspected. They were found to contain much of his personal and professional correspondence, accounts and various miscellaneous objects.

1867 The Trustees approved the loan of Hogarth's 'Election' series to the Universal Exhibition in Paris (under the terms of a special Act of Parliament) but the pictures were in the end not lent because it was decided to restrict the 'Fine Arts' section to pictures created since 1855. The large Canaletto, the Fuseli and Bird paintings were glazed and the Eastlake and Beechey pictures repaired.

1868 Library, Breakfast Room, Study and Dressing Room entirely 'renovated'. The main dome skylight and the Hogarth Room skylight covered with wire guards.

1870 Callcott's 'Passage Point' was cleaned by a Mr Merritt. Repairs were carried out to the stonework from Westminster in the Monk's Yard, as recommended by Mr Smirke.

1871 The Trustees ordered that an official dress [uniform] be provided for the manservant in addition to his wages.

1872 New iron hinges were fitted to the planes in the Picture Room, on account of the extra weight caused by glazing the pictures. The ceilings of the Drawing Rooms were repainted.

1873 The paintwork in the Monk's Parlour was re-varnished and the ceiling of the Hogarth Room re-painted. It was decided that the extra attendants employed for the season should have 'wands' like those of the attendants at the British Museum (presumably to point items out to visitors). A Mr Cooper completed a MS Catalogue of the Library (printed in 1878, see below). To preserve the remnants of Soane's 'Worcester' dinner service it was decided to buy a 'small service of ordinary ware' for general use.

1874 The opening hours were extended to 10–5 in April and May, 10–6 in June and

July and 10–5 in August. The floors of the Drawing Rooms were covered with linoleum in lieu of the carpets, which were now worn out.

1875 The Hogarths and some other paintings cleaned by J L Rutley. The Durno 'Merry Wives of Windsor' was re-lined. The two smaller Canalettos were glazed. The gems in two cases in the North Drawing Room were re-arranged on new trays. New numbers were painted on objects in the Museum, the originals having begun to rub off. Inscriptions painted on to many of the picture frames. A new range installed in the front kitchen.

1878 Joseph Bonomi died, aged 81. He had previously inserted various papers, with a letter, in one of the cinerary urns under the Dome. James Wild appointed Curator 18 April. A letter was received from Frederick Soane, son of George Soane and grandson of Sir John, regretting that the Academy had not elected him Curator and appealing for assistance. The Trustees replied that they had neither powers nor means to assist him. He was 63. A catalogue of the library was printed.

1879 The opening hours for the Museum this year were Tuesdays and Thursdays in February, March and August and Tuesdays, Thursdays and Saturdays from April to July.

1880 – 81 Trustees involved in a light and air suit with Messrs Carter when they built their seed warehouse behind the Museum, resulting in a Court Order fixing the height of that building.

1883 A number of pictures, including the Hogarths, relined at the National Gallery and cleaned by a Mr Dyer. The 'Passage Point' by Callcott was glazed.

1885 Miss Harris, the Inspectress, resigned on account of old age. Mrs Wookey appointed.

1884 Extensive work to the drainage and sanitary arrangements carried out by Messrs Dent and Hellyer (as a consequence, the Museum did not open until March). The floor boards around the margins of the Library, Breakfast Room and Museum stained and waxed. New 'oil cloth' was laid in the Museum.

1886 A cupboard in the Dressing Room, sealed by Sir John Soane and marked 'not to be opened before November 22, 1886', was opened in the presence of eight Trustees and the solicitor. It was found to contain a copy of the privately-printed memoir of Soane's troubles with his children, professional correspondence, bills, etc. Reynolds' 'Love and Beauty' cleaned by Mr Dyer and glazed.

1887 The frames of Hogarth's 'Election' series strengthened with hoop iron after the frame of 'Chairing the Member' collapsed.

1888 The antique marbles cleaned.

1889 On the termination of a lease of No. 12 it was resolved to take the room at the back (Soane's old office and original picture room) into the Museum. A design for its rebuilding and for forming a new room off the ground floor Ante-Room was prepared by the Curator, James Wild. These works, together with alterations to the second-floor rooms, were completed in the following year.

1890 Messrs Powell began to rearrange the stained glass through the Museum. An arch was opened through to the former cellar beneath the rear room of No. 12 to create the 'West Chamber'. New skylights were ordered for the main stair-cases of Nos 12 and 13. Hayward and Eckstein glass floor-lights were fixed in the Museum Corridor outside the Picture Room. The William Collins 'Charity' window was removed from the Tivoli Recess and installed in a new window opened for it in the north wall of the Shakespeare Recess (this alteration was as a result of the reduction in the depth of both recesses as part of the construction of the ground floor Ante-Room).

1891 Alterations to the basement, the so-called 'Flaxman Recess' being formed. Hogarth's 'A Rake's Progress' returned to the Picture Room and hung together above the fireplace on the East wall, the large Canaletto having been moved, along with the Callcott 'Passage Point' to the New Picture Room. Professor Roger Smith and Bannister Fletcher were given permission to have casts made from some of the more important marbles in the collection. It was decided in future to open the Museum for four days a week, Tuesday to Friday, from March to August. Saturday had been substituted for Friday since 1880 but this had not added to the number of visitors and four consecutive days would be easier to administer. A number of casts, considered redundant, were broken up and taken away. The Pompeian Model Stand was reduced in size and again moved, this time to the first floor. Dr Edwin Freshfield, one of the Trustees, gave a dinner and reception in the Museum, electric light being temporarily installed.

1892 A scheme for sweeping away the whole of the Upper Drawing Office (p.18) was proposed but abandoned as was a scheme to add a fourth storey to No. 13. The re-arrangement of the stained glass was completed: the majority of Soane's windows were removed and new windows, composed of leaded lights containing new arrangements of stained glass subject panels, substituted. James Wild died. Following his death the decorative scheme for the inside of the New Picture Room dome, for which working drawings had been prepared and Trustee approval received, was abandoned.

1893 Wyatt Angelicus Van Sandow Papworth appointed Curator. Mr John Rewe cleaned the six Meyer paintings and 16 others. Mr S Jenkins recovered the sofa and 12 chairs in the Library and Dining Room with morocco at a cost of £24 19s. The three 'carved wood tables' (in the style of William Kent) were ordered to be painted.

1894 Wyatt Papworth died. George H Birch appointed Curator. Trials were done with blue paint to fill in the hieroglyphs on the sarcophagus. Mr Marden cleaned the casts in the Upper Drawing Office.

1896 A third receptacle (a bath), sealed by Sir John Soane, was opened and found to contain family and professional papers. The 'Pasticcio' in the Monument Court was removed as it had become unstable.

1897 Electric light installed by Messrs Drake and Graham.

1900 The staircase and galleries (ie. the Dome and the Museum) painted green. The Trustees appealed unsuccessfully against payment of rates.

1902 The original Axminster carpets in the Library and Dining Room were sent away for repair and on their return partially covered with felt to protect them. On 27 September the roof over the main building was found to be on fire, perhaps caused by a 'careless plumber' at work on the roof: the damage was small. The insurance money was used to remove the old copper roof covering and to repair and recover the roof with lead. The window in the south wall of the Basement East Corridor was bricked up (re-opened in 2003).

1904 The Princess (Mary) of Wales visited the Museum. George H Birch died. Walter L Spiers appointed Curator. Sir George Birdwood, one of the additional Trustees, submitted a proposal to apply for an Act of Parliament to enable the Trustees to send the paintings to the National Gallery and the antiquities to the British Museum and to reorganise the Museum as a library of architecture. After discussion the proposal was abandoned. The first postcard of the Museum was produced. It was agreed that all the drawings in the collection should be stamped with a Museum stamp.

1905 Mrs Wookey, the Inspectress, died, and was succeeded by her daughter, Mrs Elinor M Daniell. A new fire hose installed in the basement and two additional hand pumps (each with 3 fire buckets) placed on the Ground Floor and in the South Drawing Room. The lantern light in the 'Dome' was replaced.

1907 The window in the Picture Room Recess reglazed by Powells with leaded lights.

1908 The Princess (Mary) of Wales, accompanied by her daughter, Princess Mary, visited the Museum. Wallis Budge's account of the sarcophagus published. A pair of swing doors installed between the front hall and the inner hall, replacing Soane's original single leaf door. The stained glass formerly in Soane's door was re-arranged in the swing doors.

1910 Additonal fragments of the sarcophagus lid were presented to the Museum by Professor Weidemann of Bonn.

1911 It was reported to the Trustees in June that the Pearl Life Assurance Company had purchased the property behind the Museum between Whetstone Park and Holborn including Messrs Carter's seed warehouse, then in the course of demolition, with the intention of building a large block of offices. Werner Pfleiderer and Perkins reconstructed Soane's heating apparatus fixing a new, larger furnace and converting the piping into four circulations instead of three.

1911–12 Negotiations entered into with Pearl leading to an agreement in July 1912 that the façade of the future new building on Whetstone Park be faced with white glazed brick and cleaned once a year in March or April. The foundation stone for the main Pearl Building on High Holborn, designed by H P (Percy) Monckton was laid September 1912. A new lantern light was fixed over the Hogarth Room. Morrill and son cleaned and re-varnished a number of paintings, including the Hunneman portrait of John Soane and Durno's 'Merry Wives of Windsor'.

1913 A further 7 pictures were cleaned, varnished and re-lined.

1914 First World War. The first stage of the Pearl Building completed.

1915 As a precaution against air-raid damage, 18 pictures were sent away and the sarcophagus protected by sandbags.

1917 Walter L Spiers died. Arthur T Bolton appointed Curator. The Tivoli Recess converted to a WC.

1918 Books and MSS moved on account of air-raids. The second-floor back room made into a Model Room. Pictures, books and MSS stored for protection in the Post Office Tube, returned in December. Model of Tyringham, Bucks., presented by F A König.

1919 New bookcases and plan chests made for the North Drawing Room, to centralise the architectural library (completed 1923).

1921 A T Bolton was in discussion with the Bank of England and their architects Baker and Troup about the proposed rebuilding of the Bank. The Trustees agreed to protest against any destructive alteration to Soane's design.

1922 The Basevi Notebooks were presented to the Museum. The Trustees wrote to the Bank of England to protest about the discrepancy between their undertaking to preserve Soane's Banking Halls and the published plans. Discussions continued in 1922–23 and letters of protest appeared in The Times 1923–24.

1924 A T Bolton's *The Works of Sir John Soane* published. Demolition of Soane's Bank of England, leaving only the external wall, began.

1925 HM Queen Mary, Princess Mary and the Duke of Cambridge visited the Museum. The staircase was remarbled.

1927 A T Bolton's *The Portrait of Sir John Soane* published.

1928 Soane's *Lectures on Architecture* (ed. A T Bolton) published.

1931 A new parquet floor was laid in the Drawing Rooms.

1933 The Trustees protested against the alteration (removal of the attic storey) of Soane's 'Tivoli Corner' at the Bank of England, but without effect.

1937 The exterior masonry, painted since 1839, was stripped – only the two caryatids being left painted.

1938 Two grants of £500 received from the Pilgrim Trust. The Sudeley Committee made certain criticisms of the arrangements of the Museum and its accessibility to students.

1939 Second World War. Twenty-one of the more important paintings, and four cases of drawings and MSS delivered to the National Gallery and British Museum for evacuation.

1940 The Museum was damaged by bomb blast on the night of 7–8 September: the loggia windows on the first floor were severely damaged as was the stained glass in the north window of the Dining Room and the Monk's Parlour window. Much of the original glass was destroyed. On 24–25 September an incendiary bomb broke through the boarding, entered the Dining Room by the north window and burnt the floor and carpet. It was extinguished before further damage was done. On the night of 15–16 October a land mine fell in the SE corner of Lincoln's Inn Fields and more damage was done: the front windows on the ground and first floors were blown in and William Collins' 'Charity' window was destroyed (apart from the central section of the bottom panel). The Museum was closed for the remainder of the War.

1941 In November an almost complete evacuation of the Museum began. All the architectural drawings and large cases of selected books etc. went to Lord Crawford's Haigh Hall, Wigan, Lancashire, at a cost of £54 6s.

1942 Sir Harry Verney's offer of free storage provided the Museum paid £15 p.a. towards heating costs was accepted. Ten motor vans took 250 tea chests and 22 wooden cases containing architectural models, bronzes, the smaller marbles etc., to the Tenants' Hall on the Verney Estate – Rhianva, Menai Straits, Anglesey, Wales – at a cost for transport of £585.

1945 Arthur T Bolton, Curator, died. John Newenham Summerson appointed. Mrs Daniell, Inspectress, resigned. Miss Dorothy Stroud appointed from 1 Jan 1946. In December the Curator relinquished occupation of the third floor in order for it to become a flat for the Porter (previously accommodated in the Basement kitchens). The Pompeii model and other models were moved to the old Porter's bedroom in the basement. Donation of £2,000 by the Pilgrim Trust for the reinstatement of the Museum.

1946 Second donation of £2,000 by the Pilgrim Trust. Essential war-damage repairs completed including two new lantern-lights over the Breakfast Room. By March the contents of the Museum had been returned. The Museum remained closed to the general public.

1947 The Trust funds being no longer adequate for the maintenance of the Museum, application was made to the Treasury for grant-in-aid to enable the Trustees (a) to continue to fulfil the provisions of the Act of 1833 and (b) to open the Museum on five days in the week and generally to improve its services to students. The Museum reopened after being closed to the public for 7 years on 2 September: printed cards of admission were discontinued. The re-opening coincided with the receipt of the first annual grant-in-aid from the Treasury, of £2,250. The Museum was from this date open throughout the year, except for one month in the summer (August). Parliament has made an annual grant since this date. John Summerson designed a new roof-light for the New Picture Room to replace Wild's iron dome following war damage. New roof-lights were made for the 'Old Students Room' (Upper Drawing Office) and the Museum Corridor. A stair carpet replaced linoleum on the main stairs. Various drawings were cleaned by the British Museum, the 'Charles jewel' was cleaned by Garrards and the bronze 'Triform Diana' was cleaned at the Wallace Collection. The Egyptian antiquities were catalogued by Dr Margaret Murray and the photographing of exhibits by Messrs A C Cooper (begun September 1946) continued. On May 22 1947 the first 'Short Description' written by John Summerson, was published and sold an average of 53 copies per week during the year.

1948 HM Queen Mary visited the Museum.

1949 A new skylight was made for the Picture Room Recess. The Watteau painting was cleaned by J Hell.

1950 The ruins in the Monk's Yard brushed down and treated with Cementone.

1951 The Dining Room, Library and Breakfast Room restored, the original finish being reproduced. Powell and Sons restored the west loggia window in the South Drawing Room, using the surviving stained glass and incorporating a panel recording the restoration. The sarcophagus was cleaned. Cornelius Vermeule of Harvard University began work on his Catalogue of the Antiquities in Sir John Soane's Museum.

1952 J Summerson's *Sir John Soane* published. The Curator's Annual Report records that due to lack of funds very little restoration work was carried out this year.

1953 The Study and Dressing Room restored. Dr Hell cleaned the Lawrence portrait. 50 Adam drawings were repaired at the British Museum. Cornelius Vermeule completed his Catalogue of the Antiquities. The bicentenary of Soane's birth was marked by a wreath-laying: the Royal Academy and the RIBA were invited to send wreaths. The Coronation of Elizabeth II was marked with red, white and blue flowers on the second floor front loggia. A selection of drawings by Robert Adam was lent to the Iveagh Bequest at Kenwood House – the first time they had been seen outside the Museum. The enabling provision for this loan was included in the LCC General Powers Bill.

1954 The Hogarth paintings cleaned by Dr J Hell. An Attendants' uniform was suggested. The Pearl Assurance Co. asked for the Trustees' agreement to an extension across the back of their building, under the 1912 agreement (see above). The Trustees agreed to the use of Portland Stone rather than glazed tiles.

1955 The window in the north wall of the Shakespeare Recess opened in 1890 to take the Charity window was blocked up. Dr Hell cleaned the two smaller Canaletto paintings. The *New Description* first published, a re-writing by John Summerson. It was agreed that the Porter's livery be replaced by a dark suit. HRH Princess Alexandra visited the Museum in November and the Curator reported to the Trustees that she 'took a cordial dislike to the Museum and accepted with reluctance my assurance that it was not haunted'.

1956 A selection of Soane drawings were exhibited at Kenwood House. Again, enabling provision was made in the LCC General Powers Bill.

1957 New glass light shades ('lustre bags') fitted to the Library and Dining Room in place of alabaster bowls. The first television feature on the Museum was broadcast in which 'the architecture of the Museum was brilliantly exploited by Dr Pevsner'. HRH Princess Margaret visited the Museum in March.

1958 Picture Room restored following bomb damage. The window behind the Nymph was reconstructed but because of financial constraints the decorative stained glass could not be reproduced and plain coloured glass was used instead. John Summerson knighted.

1959 The West Chamber was partitioned off with movable screens and the rear galleries (Dome area, Colonnade, Students' Room and Museum Corridor) and crypt re-decorated.

1961 D Stroud, *The Architecture of Sir John Soane,* published. The Fouquet model of the Pantheon, broken in the blitz, was repaired at the Institute of Archaeology laboratory.

1962 No. 14 Lincoln's Inn Fields offered to the Trustes for £42,500. The Curator petitioned the Treasury for an exceptional grant to enable the purchase but this was refused. No. 14 was subsequently sold at auction for £70,000.

1963 Reynolds' *Snake in the Grass* restored by Horace Buttery.

1964 New gas central-heating system installed, replacing Soane's own Perkins system.

1965 The Curator presented a memorandum to the Trustees on the possibility of the Museum occupying and using No. 12 as an extension. The Trustees resolved that this would be desirable.

1966 The two Drawing Rooms were re-decorated for the first time since 1948. To reduce overcrowding in the plan chests a new 16-drawer plan chest was commissioned and the drawings re-distributed. New linoleum was laid in the Museum. The leather chairs in the Library were re-upholstered.

1967–69 The roofs over the rear galleries were gradually re-leaded, the Curator reporting to the Trustees that 'so far as I can discover the existing lead is that laid by Soane between 1812 and 1824. Its long life may be accounted for by the sheltered site of the rear galleries which receive little sun'. The Picture Room roof was recovered in 1967–68, the Old Students' Room (Upper Drawing Office) in 1968–69 and the Breakfast Room in 1969.

1968 Dorothy Stroud, Inspectress, awarded the MBE.

1969 No. 12 Lincoln's Inn Fields re-occupied by the Trustees with a view to extending the Museum. On 1 April the Soane Museum Act of 1833 was superseded by a Scheme ordered by the Secretary of State for Education and Science under the Charities Act, 1960. From December the Museum employed a night guard for the first time.

1970 A fragment of badly-decayed arcading removed from the Monk's Yard to a position inside the Museum (at the north end of the West Corridor in the Crypt).

1971 Restoration and equipping of No. 12 Lincoln's Inn Fields completed with grants from the Department of Education and Science and the Pilgrim Trust (£2,000) towards the restoration of the Breakfast Room where Crace's painted ceiling emerged from a covering of ten or more coats of whitewash. Public lavatories were created in the original rear kitchen of No. 13. No. 13 was re-wired and the main roof re-leaded. The Research Library having moved into No. 12 Lincoln's

Inn Fields, the two Drawing Rooms were reconstituted. A replica chandelier was purchased for the South Drawing Room. The *Rake's Progress* and *Election* series paintings were lent to the 'Hogarth' Exhibition at the Tate Gallery. Christina Scull joined the Museum as Library Assistant.

1972 Following an outbreak of dry rot in the party wall between the Picture Room and No. 15, the flush panelling on the east wall of the Picture Room was removed and the panelling and wall treated by Rentokil.

1973 The Picture Room was redecorated and unsuccessful experiments carried out with non-reflecting glass on one large (Election) and one small (Rake) Hogarth painting.

1974 The façade of No. 13 was cleaned. Cornelius Vermeule's Catalogue of Antiquities was distributed in a limited typescript edition, with revisions up to 1973. A C Cooper began a systematic 'photographic inventory' of the Museum's contents.

1975 The Museum was open throughout August for the first time. The Dining Room ceiling was restored and the Dressing Room completely re-decorated including re-graining of the walls and ceiling. The work was carried out by G Jackson and Sons who redecorated these rooms in 1951. The New Picture Room was also redecorated. Turner's watercolour of the 'Val d'Aosta' was cleaned at the British Museum and between early 1974 and the end of March 1975 about 300 Soane drawings were de-acidified and repaired at the Public Record Office.

1976 The Dome, Colonnade, Museum Corridor and Students' Room (Upper Drawing Office) were re-decorated for the first time since 1959. The Picture Room Recess was also redecorated. A further 365 drawings by Soane and Dance were de-acidified at the PRO.

1978 Mr and Mrs Koralek carried out a systematic programme of picture frame repair in 1978–79. The main roof of No. 12 was re-leaded.

1981 The exterior parts of the two houses were re-decorated (first time since 1974).

1982 The rear elevation on to Whetstone Park was cleaned by Dove Brothers.

1983 The Breakfast Room was restored by G Jackson and Sons, the same firm who carried out the last restoration of the room in 1951.

1984 Sir John Summerson, Curator, retired. Peter Kai Thornton appointed in his stead. Miss Dorothy Stroud, Inspectress and Assistant Curator retired. Mrs Margaret Schuelein began work as Paper Conservator.

1985 Mrs Margaret Richardson appointed Inspectress and Deputy Curator.

1986 North and South Drawing Rooms re-decorated, re-creating Soane's original 'patent yellow' and bronze green colours following paint analysis by Dr Ian

Bristow. The yellow silk curtains were recreated by Elizabeth Eaton Limited (sponsored by The Leche Trust) using the evidence of archive bills and water-colour views. The sofa was recovered to match the curtains. New Model Room established on second floor of No. 12 Lincoln's Inn Fields. Tipu Sahib's ivory furniture (p.63) restored by Messrs Spink and Sons. Portrait of Sir John Soane by Lawrence surface-cleaned by Mr H Lank. Danby *Merchant of Venice* surface-cleaned by Sally Lescher. Dr Eileen Harris began the cataloguing of Soane's Architectural Library. The Head Porter, Mr Hancock, died. Captain Anthony Smith was appointed as Resident Warden. Miss Helen Dorey joined the Museum's staff.

1987 The 150th anniversary of Soane's death and the Museum's inception. A wreath was laid at the Soane tomb on the 20 January, the day of his death. On the same day Pitzhanger Manor, Soane's country house at Ealing, opened to the public as a museum. The Trustees gave a dinner to mark the anniversary, attended by the Minister for the Arts and a one-day Soane Symposium was held at The Society of Antiquaries, Burlington House. Sir John Summerson was made a Companion of Honour. On 6 February the Metropolitan Police foiled an attempted armed robbery at the Museum. The roof of No. 12 Lincoln's Inn Fields was repaired and the façade cleaned. Sir John Soane's Museum Society was set up as a charitable company to promote and raise funds for the Museum. Ward's *Portrait of Fanny* was cleaned. *Van Tromp's Barge* was cleaned by Lord Dunluce and the frame was restored and re-gilded. All twelve Hogarths were lent to The Tate Gallery for their 'Manners and Morals' Exhibition. The Conservation department at the Tate surface-cleaned the paintings and the frames of the *Election* series were restored. The Picture Room closed in October for repair and re-decoration (sponsored by the Bank of England to mark the bi-centenary of Soane's appoint-ment as Architect) during the absence of the Hogarths. The room was re-painted in the original olive-green following paint analysis. The architect was Julian Harrap and the works were carried out by Clark and Fenn Limited. Nicholas Savage began working alongside Eileen Harris on the Architectural Library Catalogue.

1988 The following oil paintings were cleaned: Callcott, *Thames below Greenwich;* Bird, *The Cheat Detected;* Zuccarelli, *Landscape;* Eastlake, *Una and the Red Cross Knight;* Beechey, *Sir Francis Bourgeois;* Cosway, *Persian Lady;* Thornhill, *Ceiling Design;* Flaxman, *Copy of Cartoon Fragment;* Fuseli, *The Count of Ravenna;* Hamilton, *The Landing of Richard II* and Jackson's portraits of *John Soane in his masonic robes* and *Mrs Soane.* The frames were restored and in some cases re-gilded. The restoration of the Picture Room was completed and in October the

Trustees gave a reception to mark the re-opening. The frame of Danby's *Scene from the Merchant of Venice* was restored and re-gilded. The front doors of Nos 12 and 13 were re-painted the original bronze green as was the door of No. 14, the third Soane home (occupied by Messrs Needham and Grant, Solicitors). Showcases were installed in the Ante-Room to display small objects from Soane's collection. Weatherall, Green and Smith, Chartered Surveyors, sponsored and carried out a complete survey of the Museum's fabric. Finch Allibone catalogued the Soane models and Maya Hambly Soane's drawing instruments. Judith Maher was appointed Resident Warden.

1989 Susan Palmer joined the Museum as Archivist. Sir John Soane's Museum Society appointed Julian Spicer as Fundraiser. The new Model Room on the second floor of No. 12 was completed. This displayed almost 100 models previously not on view. The work was carried out by Murray John Architects. Compton Hall Restoration cleaned the Dome balustrade to reveal the original coloured finishes (p.59). Soane's three Axminster carpets (p.10) were also cleaned. The Hogarth paintings were fitted with low-reflecting glass. The survey of the fabric carried out in 1988 was costed at £1.6 million over five years. The Trustees launched a campaign to raise £2.5 million to cover this and the conservation of the rooms and contents. At a Press Conference on 23 November, James Tuckey, Managing Director of MEPC plc, and Richard Luce, MP, Minister for the Arts, announced their intention to fund the restoration of the fabric over five years. Julian Harrap was officially appointed Architect to the Museum for this project.

1990 Work began on Phase I of the fabric restoration: the rear roofs and skylights. The restoration of the Shakespeare Recess was completed. The architect in charge was Murray John, RIBA. The two Howard paintings from the Recess were cleaned and their frames re-gilded. The restoration of the Study and Dressing Room began in the autumn following paint sections and a detailed study of the arrangement of the rooms in Soane's day. The walls were repainted their original red with bronze green shelving. The sash windows were restored to their original configurations and a high shelf across in front of the Study window reinstated. Doorways were restored to their original dimensions. Coloured glass was put back in windows and skylights, linoleum removed from the floors and the boards whitened and sealed. The mahogany pump case and washstand in the Dressing Room were recreated using an original a pump of *c*.1812. The marbles and casts were cleaned by Holden Conservation Limited and their frames cleaned or re-painted by Jane Wilkinson. Casts reproducing missing finials etc. were taken by Taylor Pearce Restoration Ltd. The rooflight model set into the Dressing Room ceiling was cleaned. The two stained glass panels of the

'Creation' and the 'Last Judgement' originally in the Dining Room window and presumed destroyed in World War II were discovered in the Basement and re-hung in their original positions. Soane's Axminster carpet in the Library was mended. New stair-carpet, re-creating as nearly as possible Soane's own, was woven and laid. A recreation of Soane's Drawing Room carpet was also woven and laid by Woodward Grosvenor Limited using the original pattern from the Kidderminster Archives. A condition survey of the Museum's oil paintings was carried out. Martin Holden cleaned the Bullock bust of Shakespeare and subse-quently re-painted it. Helen Dorey was appointed to the Curatorial staff. Esther Caplin completed the typological classifying of the catalogue sheets for the works of art (up to 1990 filed in room by room order as inventoried by Bailey in 1837). Lynda Fairbairn was appointed for three years to catalogue the Museum's Italian Renaissance drawings. Angela Thompson was engaged to clean and re-furbish books from Soane's architectural library. The Museum entered into a deed with the Pearl Assurance Company to control future development on their site with regard to the height, profile and facing materials of the building behind the Museum.

1991 The restoration of the Study and Dressing Room was completed. Work contin-ued on the Five-year Restoration project. The marquetry case of the Threlkeld clock (see p.64) and the eight Cantonese Chairs (see p.8) were restored. Samuel Scott's *View on the River Thames* was cleaned. Viola Pemberton-Piggott began cleaning the museum's three Canaletto paintings (completed 1992). The frames of the Canalettos and Calcott's *The Passage Point* and the Downman portraits of Mrs Soane senior and John Soane junior were restored. Work began on the restoration of the stained glass panels from the Breakfast Room central skylight and the Monk's Parlour window. *The Soane Hogarths*, by Christina Scull, was published in July.

1992 In January phase 2 of the five-year restoration work to the front façade of No. 13 Lincoln's Inn Fields began. The contract was awarded to Messrs Falkner and Son Ltd. The projecting Portland stone loggia was found to be sound with the exception of small sections of the top balustrade where cracking of stone had exposed some of the original iron cramps. However the stonework was discoloured and the incised decoration clogged with remnants of paint applied between 1839 and 1937. The opportunity was taken to replace post-war modern glass with 'plate' glass (obtained by Soane for his main front windows) or crown glass (used by Soane for the less important upper windows). The origi-nal stained glass window on the second floor (removed *c.*1892) was put back into the loggia. Stained glass borders were restored to the east loggia window on the first floor. The Coade Stone caryatids were cleaned and re-painted, and the four Gothic corbels from Westminster conserved and whitewashed. The restoration of the 'Monk's Cell', used as a storeroom since the 19th century, was begun. The panelling was reinstated (reproducing one surviving section) and the mirrored opening casements, giving views to the Monk's Parlour, over-hauled and restored. The large Monk's Parlour window, taken out in the 1890s, was recreated: the 16th-century subject panels had survived in store. The restoration work in the Monk's Parlour and the Monk's Cell was funded by a grant from the Wolfson Foundation, the Wolfson Family Charitable Trust and the Office of Arts and Libraries. The New Picture Room was re-decorated and re-arranged, with additional objects put on display. The New Picture Room ceiling was painted by Alan Dodd, following the intentions of the architect, James Wild (Curator 1876–92), whose scheme for a painted ceiling, although approved by the Trustees, was thwarted by his death. Peter Thornton and Helen Dorey published *A Miscellany of Objects from Sir John Soane's Museum*. Sir John Summerson died on 10 November 1992.

1993 Phase 3 of the Building Restoration Programme, the restoration of the Ground floor of No. 12 and opening up of a 'Link Passage' to the Ante-Room in No. 13, began in April. The ground floor front room of No. 12 was prepared to receive the new 'Gallery' showcases: the floor was strengthened; a false door converted to a real opening to aid circulation and window sashes and shutters restored. The fanlights over the front door and inner halls in No. 12 were restored by John Sambrook. A showcase was installed in the Link Passage to display small items. Pauline Plummer began the cleaning and restoration of the ceiling of No. 12 Breakfast Room. *The Opening of London Bridge* by George Jones was cleaned and two Kent tables restored. An independent *Review* of the Museum was commissioned by the Department of National Heritage. Sir John Soane's Museum Foundation (New York) raised funds in America for the restoration of the No. 12 Breakfast Room.

1994 Phases 4 and 5 of the Five-year Restoration programme began in June, consist-ing of the cleaning and restoration of the rear façades of Nos 12 and 13, the Whetstone Park façade of Nos 12 to 14 and the high-level Roofs. This work included cleaning the brick façades, restoration of windows and joinery and renewal of lead on the top roof. In tandem, new security systems and flood-light-ing were installed and water-tanks and pipes re-located and rationalised. Floors were reinstated in the 'lift-shaft' created by Sir John Summerson in 1970–71 in No. 12 and the main services risers were installed in the shaft. Plain red stained glass borders were re-created in the North Drawing Room windows, following the evidence of the 1837 AB Inventory. Red glass borders were also reinstated in the top staircase window of No. 13. Work continued on the design of the 'Soane Gallery' in the front floor room of No. 12 by Eva Jiricna Architects. The Catacombs in the basement were recreated under the direction of Murray John Architects. The restoration of the Dome area and Colonnade began, sponsored by The Foundation for Sport and the Arts. The walls were repainted by Wilm and Joy Huning and the antique sculpture was cleaned by Holden Conservation Limited. Linoleum was removed from the floors. The painted surfaces of the casts were cleaned. Metal plates were added beneath the wooden shelves which project from the balustrade and support heavy marble items and each item re-fixed on a tall metal spike. The restoration of the No. 12 Breakfast Room ceiling was completed and the walls were then painted, following paint analysis. The restored room was then furnished to resemble the 1798 view by J M Gandy, including a reproduction of the original desk. The completion of the No. 12 Breakfast Room and the Link Passage showcases were generously sponsored by Sir John Soane's Museum Foundation (New York), The Museum and Galleries Improvement Fund and the Farmly Trust. The No. 12 rear hall and staircase were redecorated following paint analysis. A sixteenth-century Flemish carved wooden crucifixion scene was restored and installed in the Monk's Cell. A number of early 19th-century lamps were purchased in order to provide more appropriate lighting in a number of interiors. A new plaster rosette was designed and manufactured for the Breakfast Room octagonal lantern light. The Nymph Recess window was restored, funded by the John and Ruth Howard Charitable Trust. Canaletto's *Riva degli Schiavoni* was loaned to *The Glory of Venice* exhibition at the Royal Academy. Sally Jeffery catalogued the Mansion House drawings in the Museum's collection. Alison Shell began working alongside Eileen Harris and Nicholas Savage on the cataloguing of Soane's Library. *Sir John Soane's Museum* by Stefan Buzas and Richard Bryant, was published.

1995 The Five-year Programme of restoration of the fabric was completed on time and within the budget in April. A party was held to mark the completion of the work, to celebrate the opening of the Soane Gallery and to mark the retirement of Peter Thornton as Curator. Margaret Richardson was appointed Curator. Helen Dorey was appointed Inspectress and Deputy Curator. The installation of the Soane Gallery was completed in February–March. Christina Scull, the Librarian, left the Museum's staff and Susan Palmer, the Museum's Archivist, took over the running of the Library. Two new posts were created: Christopher Woodward was appointed Assistant Curator (Education) and Stephen Astley was appointed Assistant Curator (Drawings) with particular responsibility for the cataloguing of the Robert Adam drawings. Ian Batten was appointed to the new post of Finance Officer. The first exhibition in the new Soane Gallery was *Soane: Connoisseur and Collector* followed by *Buildings in Progress: Soane's Views of Construction.* The restoration of the Dome area was completed. Fibre-optic lighting was installed in the Colonnade and beneath the skylights around the Dome. Michael McCoy cleaned the Vulliamy Clock. Several items were restored to the positions they occupied at the time of Soane's death: a cast of the Venus de Medici (to the Crypt); a corner cupboard (to the basement hall); the Cawdor Vase (to the north window sill in the Dining Room), the Astronomical Clock (to the Library pier table), and the bronze Mercury (to the staircase). A rolling programme of maintenance work to the fabric was initiated following the completion of the Five-year Restoration Programme. The Old Kitchen was restored and converted into a small lecture theatre. An educational programme was initiated with quarterly series of lunch-time 'Gallery talks' and regular early evening Study Group meetings.

1996   The Heritage Lottery Fund awarded the Museum a grant to buy the freehold of No. 14 Lincoln's Inn Fields which was announced by the Minister for the Arts, The Rt Hon. Virginia Bottomley, JP, MP, at the Museum on 14 November. A Flaxman bas-relief *Mercury conveying Pandora to Epimethus* (M948), broken in 1942, was mended and replaced in its original position in the Dome area. The two Roman urns from the Dome area were repaired and surface-cleaned. The marble bust of Sir William Chambers by Richard Westmacott was cleaned. Jill Lever began the cataloguing of the George Dance drawings. Professor Alan Tait began the cataloguing of the Adam Grand Tour drawings. Dr David Watkin published *Sir John Soane: Enlightenment Thought and the Royal Academy Lectures* and delivered the first Annual Soane Lecture on the same subject. A leaflet on Soane's London was published jointly by the Bank of England, Dulwich Picture Gallery, Pitzhanger Manor and the Museum. Exhibitions held this year were *Soane Revisited: A Journey of Rediscovery of the Buildings of John Soane* and *Robert Adam the Creative Mind: from the sketch to the finished drawing.*

1997 Peter Thornton was appointed CBE for 'services to Sir John Soane's Museum'. Ian Batten left the Museum and Roderick Smith was appointed as his successor. *The Soanes at Home: Domestic Life at Lincoln's Inn Fields* by Susan Palmer was published. The Department of Archaeology, University of Oxford, sponsored the photography of the Museum's collection of classical and neo-classical gems. A complete survey of the Cast Store was carried out with a view to conserving all the items and putting them back on display in the Museum. The Heritage

Lottery Fund awarded the Museum a grant towards the cost of drawing up a Conservation Plan for the restoration of the three courtyards. Charles Brooking and Helen Dorey drew up a detailed report on the history of the joinery and windows in the areas surrounding the courtyard. Dr Kenneth Gray joined the Museum to assist with fundraising and the development of No. 14. The Duke of Grafton, KG, FSA retired as Chairman of the Trustees after 22 years. Richard Griffiths was elected Chairman and took office on 2 October. Miss Dorothy Stroud MBE, Inspectress of the Soane Museum 1946–84, died on 27 December. The Museum launched its website. Exhibitions held this year were *The Rake's Progress: From Hogarth to Hockney* and *The Soanes at Home: A Day in the Life of Regency London.*

1998 Lynda Fairbairn's two-volume catalogue *Italian Renaissance Drawings from the Collection of Sir John Soane's Museum* was published along with the Museum's first scholarly picture book on the *The North Italian Album*. A second picture book entitled *The Soane Canalettos* by J G Links was also published. A large painting by James Durno, *A Scene from the Merry Wives of Windsor* and its frame were restored. The housekeeper's bureau (XF39) was restored and put back in its original position in the Front Kitchen. The first phase in the renewal of the Museum's Security systems was carried out. The National Monuments Record carried out a photographic survey of the Museum. The Museum received the research papers of Miss Dorothy Stroud; following her death she left a generous legacy to the Museum. Exhibitions held this year were *A Renaissance Enigma: The North Italian Album* and *William Kent: A Poet on Paper.*

1999 In December all the collections of the Museum were designated as being of pre-eminent national importance under the MGC/DCMS Designation Scheme. An exhibition of the work of *Frank O. Gehry* was held in the Soane Gallery in May; the drawing rooms were transformed into a re-creation of Gehry's office, displaying his working models and videos illustrating his design process. From September to December the first major Soane exhibition, *John Soane: Master of Space and Light* was held at the Royal Academy curated by Margaret Richardson with MaryAnne Stevens of the RA. The installation, designed by Piers Gough, featured new models of the Bank and other Soane projects. Almost all the exhibits came from the Soane Museum: the first time that most of them had left the building since the early 19th century. To coincide with the Royal Academy exhibition, the Soane Gallery mounted *Inspired by Soane*, an exhibition featuring the work of modern architects including Juan Navarro Baldeweg, Raphael Moneo, Richard MacCormac and Richard Meier. In

December the exhibition of cutting-edge works of art entitled *Retrace your Footsteps: Remember Tomorrow,* curated by Hans-Ulrich Obrist, was installed in the Museum – with works of sculpture, paintings and film and video installations by artists including Anish Kapoor, Gilbert and George, Steve McQueen, Richard Hamilton and Isaac Julien. Other exhibitions held in the Soane Gallery during the year were *Primitive Types: The Sans Serif Alphabet from John Soane to Eric Gill* and *A Vision of Ruin: An Exhibition of Architectural Fantasies and Designs for Garden Follies.* The restoration of the Picture Room Recess (or Nymph Recess) began in April. The recess was repainted in its original colour scheme and the original arrangement of pictures, including Turner's *Val D'Aosta* and Watteau's *L'Accordée du Village,* was rehung. The Nymph was cleaned and all the small objects which at the time of Soane's death stood on the shelf round the recess were cleaned and restored to their positions. A blind was installed across the Picture Room Recess skylight using 19th-century fixings which remained *in situ.* The opportunity was taken to clean and polish the walls of the Monk's Parlour and to check the fixings of all items and a number of pieces missing from the Parlour since the mid-19th century were restored to their original positions. Patricia Jackson restored two cork models of Etruscan tombs (M1085 and M1088) and also mended an unusual Roman vessel (MP76), whose many fragments had been lying inside a cinerary urn in the Monk's Parlour since it was broken in the early 20th century. In July the Trustees purchased a sketchbook of J M Gandy dated *c.*1806 and including drawings of Rosslyn Chapel and designs for buildings at Storrs Hall, Windermere with the help of the NACF. A Conservation Plan for the restoration of the Museum's three courtyards was completed and submitted to the Heritage Lottery Fund.

2000   The Royal Academy exhibition *John Soane: Master of Space and Light* was shown at the Centro Palladio in Vicenza. Phase 2 of the renewal of the Museum's security systems was carried out early in the year. The approximately one hundred objects in the Cast Store were cleaned and mended, with the aim of replacing the majority in the Museum by the end of the year. The watercolour by Westall of 'Milton Dictating to his Daughters' was cleaned and its frame restored in memory of Brian Dyckhof. Lynda Fairbairn was awarded the Alice Davis Hitchcock Medallion of the SAHGB for her Catalogue of the Museum's Renaissance drawings. The Museum purchased Sir John Summerson's Library and an album of landscape watercolour sketches by J M Gandy, which had been given by him to his friend Sir Richard Westmacott, with the help of the NACF. William Palin was appointed Assistant Curator (Education). Jane Monahan joined the Museum for six months in February to carry out a feasibility study into future education for children in No. 14. Exhibitions held this year were *Hellman at the Soane* and *Robert Adam's Castles*.

2001 A successful bid was made to the Heritage Lottery Fund for a major grant for the restoration of the Three Courtyards. A stained glass panel of St Cecilia from the inner hall fanlight, broken in World War II, was mended and reinstated. An antique altar to Hercules (M506) was cleaned and put back in its original position. The original frame for a composite view of Soane's design for a National Monument was discovered in store, restored and the picture replaced in it. Three exhibitions were held: *Libeskind at the Soane*; *Hogarth's Election Entertainment: Artists at the Hustings*, for which Hogarth's *Election* paintings were moved to the Soane Gallery; and *Marble Mania: Sculpture Galleries in England 1640–1840*. The Royal Academy Soane exhibition was shown in Paris, Montreal and Madrid. The *Election* exhibition was shown at the Laing Art Gallery in Newcastle: the first time the *Election* paintings had ever left London.

2002 Preparatory works for the restoration of the three courtyards were carried out: the medieval ruins in the Monk's Yard were surveyed, the *pasticcio* foundations investigated (the column stood on a well shaft) and opening up works revealed the original curve of the Flaxman Recess skylight. The free-standing sculpture from the courtyards was removed and surface-cleaned. Contractors for the main project, Ellmer Construction Limited, were appointed. The 1837 arrangement of pictures within the south planes of the Picture Room was re-instated. A large papier-mâché coat of arms was re-hung in its original position on the stairs down to the basement. Six paintings of Sicilian temples by Luigi Mayer were restored. The following exhibitions were held: *Linda Karshan at the Soane: Prints and Drawings 1997–2002*; *Will Alsop at the Soane: Beauty, Joy and the Real*; *England's Lost Houses*, an exhibition of photographs from the *Country Life* Picture Library and *Sphere: loans from nvisible Museum*. The Concise Catalogue of the Museum's 30,000 drawings was made available via the Museum's website. Mike Nicholson was appointed as Development Director, employed by Sir John Soane's Museum Society

2003 The 250th anniversary of Soane's birth was celebrated with special displays of treasures in the Research Library, a 'Birthday' dinner at Lincoln's Inn and a special BBC2 programme on Soane. The main contract for the restoration of the Three Courtyards began on site in February. Work began on the re-carving of the missing elements of the *pasticcio*. Work also began on the renewal of the heating and lighting services in the basement and at the rear of the Museum. The following exhibitions were held: *John Soane and the Wooden Bridges of Switzerland: Architecture and the Culture of Technology from Palladio to the*

Grubenmanns; *John Flaxman: Master of the Purest Line*; *Bob the Roman: Heroic Antiquity and the Architecture of Robert Adam*; *Architecture Unshackled: George Dance the Younger*. The Catalogue of the Dance drawings, by Jill Lever, was published, as was *Piranesi, Paestum and Soane* by Professor John Wilton-Ely. A French version of the *Short Description* was produced. Stephen Massil joined the Museum (on a three-year contract) to catalogue the 'General Library'.

2004 The re-created *pasticcio* was installed in the Monument Court on 18 April. The restoration of the Three Courtyards was completed in October. The Crypt and rear of the Museum were re-wired, new heating installed and re-decorated. The 'Richmond' mummy case was placed in its original position, in the Sepulchral Chamber, on its original stand (identified after being in use else-where for many years). Works of art taken down for the Three Courtyards project were re-hung and the original arrangement of casts re-instated in the Basement Ante-Room and in the re-created Basement South Passage Recess. Serious structural problems were identified in the Basement East Corridor and Museum Corridor when work began to remove and replace the 1891 glass floor-lights: work had to be postponed until 2005 and the Picture Room was closed for much of the year (the Hogarths were put into store). The following exhibitions were held: *William West and the Regency Toy Theatre*; *Saving Wotton: the remarkable story of a Soane Country House*; *Alessi at the Soane: Tea and Coffee Towers* and *Raymond Erith: Progressive Classicist*. An exhibition of books from Soane's Library, *Hooked on Books*, was mounted at the University of Nottingham. The catalogue of the Museum's stained glass was published as a special issue of *The Journal of Stained Glass*.

2005 Replicas of Soane's 1822 Axminster Carpets were laid in the Library-Dining Room, enabling the whole room to be open to the public. Margaret Richardson retired as Curator in April and was awarded the OBE. Tim Knox was appointed Director. The Monk's Yard ruins were cleaned, consolidated and lime-washed (Taylor Pearce Restoration). The pebble and bottle-top paving was also conserved and a new section laid through the passage out to the Monk's Yard. Structural repairs were carried out in the Museum Corridor and Basement East Corridor with the help of an emergency grant from the DCMS: the works of art were removed, the panelling taken down and the brick walls repaired. The new stone floor slabs were then installed: they were slid in horizontally via the Whetstone Park doors with inches to spare. The columns and capitals at the east end of the Crypt were then re-installed and the re-created railing installed between them. The work was completed in February 2006. The following exhibitions were held: *Thomas Banks (1735–1805): Britain's first modern sculptor*;

Wright to Gehry: Drawings from the collection of Barbara Pine; *The Regency Country House, from the archives of Country Life*. Dr Gordon Higgott began a 15-month secondment from English Heritage cataloguing the English Baroque architectural drawings in the Museum, which were digitally photographed for the project.

2006 Work began on the restoration of No. 14 Lincoln's Inn Fields, to be completed in summer 2007 (contractors: Fullers Builders Ltd). The following exhibitions were held: *Pistrucci's 'Capriccio': a Rediscovered Masterpiece Regency Sculpture*; *Soane's Magician: The Tragic Genius of Joseph Michael Gandy*; *First and Last Loves: John Betjeman and Architecture*. The original arrangement of busts and other antiquities was reinstated around the sarcophagus in the Sepulchral Chamber, and the display of busts on tables in the Basement Ante-Room was also put back. The catalogue entries for the *Hooked on Books* exhibition were published online, the first tranche of the Soane Library catalogue to be made available on the Museum's website.

2007 The restoration of No. 14 Lincoln's Inn Fields was completed in the summer. Stephanie Coane was appointed Librarian and Bethany Kingston Education Manager. The Museum's 12 Hogarth paintings were lent to Tate Britain from February to April. In exchange, Turner's large *Forum Romanum, for Mr. Soane's Museum*, lent to the Museum by Tate Britain, was exhibited at the Soane for the first time, as the centrepiece of a small exhibition in the Old Kitchen (*Soane and Turner: Illuminating a Friendship*). The Museum's first online catalogue (the designs for Greenwich Hospital, part of the English Baroque architectural drawings catalogue) was made available. Groups of drawings by Soane and Adam, the Soane sketchbooks and Adam's Grand Tour drawings, were digitally photographed in preparation for further online catalogues. Also the Museum's photographic archive was digitised. The following exhibitions were held: *Visions of World Architecture: John Soane's Royal Academy Lecture Illustrations*; *A Passion for Building: The Amateur Architect in England 1650–1850*. George Jones' *The Smoking House at Chelsea* was cleaned and its frame restored and the cork models were cleaned prior to new digital photography. Work began on the conversion of the West Chamber as a store for works of art.

THE SOANE MUSEUM ACT OF PARLIAMENT, 1833

The Act (3° Gul. IV, Cap iv) under which the Museum was founded, and under which it was administered till 1969 is entitled as follows:

An Act for settling and preserving Sir John Soane's Museum, Library and Works of Art, in Lincoln's Inn Fields in the county of Middlesex, for the Benefit of the Public, and for establishing a sufficient Endowment for the due Maintenance of the same.

This bill was introduced in the House of Commons by Joseph Hume, the Radical politician and economist. At the committee stage, George Soane gave evidence, protesting that his father had been 'improperly importuned and persuaded' to take a step which would leave himself and his family destitute. A petition was presented in the Commons on his behalf by William Cobbett, who opposed the Bill on the issue that it was morally wrong for a man to divert his estate from his family and that Parliament should not countenance such a proceeding. There was some support for this view, but Sir Robert Peel cordially welcomed Soane's benefaction, suggesting, however, that it would be better if he gave the collection to the British Museum instead of endowing a separate establishment. With the support of Lord John Russell, he proposed a clause leaving Soane free to adopt this course should he become so inclined; the clause was agreed to and the Bill received Royal Assent on 20 April 1833.

The Act vests the house and its contents in Trustees who are to give free access to it 'at least on two days in every week throughout the months of April, May and June, and at such other times as the said Trustees shall direct, to Amateurs and Students in Painting, Sculpture and Architecture . . . for consulting and inspecting and benefiting by the said collection. The Trustees and their successors shall not (except in Case of absolute Necessity) suffer the arrangement in which the said Museum . . . shall be left . . . to be altered.' Sir John is to invest £30,000 in Trust, the income, together with the rent from No. 12 Lincoln's Inn Fields, being applied to the maintenance of the Museum and the payment of salaries to a Curator and Inspectress. The first Curator and Inspectress are to be nominated by Sir John Soane's will [they were his chief clerk, George Bailey, and his old friend and housekeeper, Mrs Conduitt]. Subsequent curators are to be appointed by the President and Council of the Royal Academy, who are to select 'an English Architect who may have distinguished himself or gained any Academic Prize'. The

Curator is to have the custody of the house and collection and to keep is 'as nearly as possible in the state in which Sir John Soane shall leave it'. The following four life Trustees are appointed: Samuel Thornton, Esq.; Francis Chantrey, Esq.; Samuel Higham, Esq.; John Laurens Bicknell, Esq. Five additional Trustees are to be elected for periods of five years, by the following bodies: the Corporation of the City of London; the Royal Society; the Royal Academy, the Society of Antiquaries, and the Society of Arts. Sir John Soane's grandson, John Soane, is to be permitted to reside in the house, with his family, on attaining the age of 25, but is only to be allowed the use of the library if he follows the profession of architect [John Soane, junior, did make application to live in the house in 1847, but died soon afterwards].

Fig. 60: Interior of a mausoleum by C-L Clérisseau, 1773 (see p.34)
Photograph: Geremy Butler

APPENDIX III

THE CHARITIES (SIR JOHN SOANE'S MUSEUM) ORDER
1969

This statutory instrument (1969 No. 468) was laid before Parliament in draft and the Order subsequently made on 26 March 1969, coming into operation on 1 April of that year. The Order was amended in 1996 and 2003. The Scheme relates to the Foundation called Sir John Soane's Museum and its provisions 'are hereby substituted for the provision of the . . . Act' of 1833 (see Appendix II) 'and accordingly the Foundation and its endowment . . . shall henceforth be administered in conformity with this Scheme under the name of Sir John Soane's Museum'. There shall be nine Trustees comprising:–

FOUR Life Trustees and

FIVE representative Trustees, to be appointed;–

ONE by the Lord Mayor and Court of Aldermen of the City of London;

ONE by the President and Council of the Royal Academy of Arts;

ONE by the President and Council of the Royal Society;

ONE by the President and Council of the Society of Antiquaries;

& ONE by the Council of the Society for the Encouragement of Arts, Manufactures and Commerce (commonly called 'The Royal Society of Arts').

A Representative Trustee 'need not be a member of the body by which he was appointed . . . [and] every Representative Trustee shall be appointed for a term of office of five years at a meeting convened and held according to the ordinary practice of the appointing body. Every future Life Trustee appointed after the 24th May 1996 shall be appointed under . . . a resolution passed . . . by a majority of not less than two-thirds of all the Trustees and shall hold office until . . . the age of 75 years'. Trustees should not 'take or hold any interest in any property belonging to the Foundation, otherwise than as a trustee'.

The Trustees 'shall hold at least two ordinary meetings each year' and a quorum exists 'when three Trustees, including at least one Life Trustee', are present at a meeting. 'Within the limits prescribed by this Scheme the Trustees shall have power to make, alter and revoke rules for the management of the foundation and to regulate their procedure.'

'The object of the Foundation shall be the provision and maintenance at Numbers 12 and 13, Lincoln's Inn Fields in Greater London of a public Museum, Library and Art Gallery, (hereinafter referred to as 'the Museum') and of such ancillary facilities including, without prejudice to the generality of the foregoing, the provision of facilities for education, including lectures, meetings and classes, as the Trustees may from time to time think fit. Moreover the books, manuscripts, prints, drawings, pictures, models, and works of art and other objects of the like kind which the Trustees may from time to time acquire for the purposes of the Foundation shall be held upon trust to be used for the general purpose of the Museum.'

'The Trustees shall have the general management and control of the Museum and may, subject as hereinafter provided, take such action as they deem expedient with a view to the better exhibition therein of the objects from time time belonging to the Foundation or any of them, including the removal of objects exhibited at the date of this Scheme in Number 13 Lincoln's Inn Fields for exhibition in Number 12 Lincoln's Inn Fields:

'Provided that in taking any action under this clause the Trustees shall have regard to the principle that Number 13 Lincoln's Inn Fields shall be maintained as nearly as circumstances will admit in the state and condition in which it was at the date of the death of the founder, Sir John Soane, in January 1837.

'The Trustees may in their absolute discretion temporarily withdraw from exhibition objects for the time being belonging to the Foundation.'

'The Trustees shall appoint and pay a Curator of the Museum, who shall be a person approved for the purpose by the Royal Academy of Arts. The Curator shall be responsible to the Trustees for the efficient conduct and working of the Museum. The appointment of the Curator shall be for such period and subject to such terms and conditions as the Trustees shall think fit.'

'The Trustees shall, in consultation with the Curator, appoint an Inspectress, a Junior Assistant Curator and such other staff as appear to them to be necessary to ensure the efficient conduct and working of the Museum . . . [they] may receive any additional funds including subscriptions, grants, donations or other endowments for the general purpose of the Foundation or for any special objects connected therewith. Such additional funds may be received on conditions which allow or require them to be applied as income or require their investment with a view to the application of the resulting income. The Trustees shall apply any sums received from public funds for the general or special purposes of the Foundation as any conditions subject to which such sums are made available may require.'

'The Trustees and all other persons capable of being bound by this Scheme shall, unless the Secretary of State for Education and Science otherwise in writing directs, do all such acts as may be necessary in order to vest in and transfer to the Official Custodian for Charities all freehold and leasehold lands and hereditaments and all stocks, shares, funds and securities at any time belonging to the Foundation. The Trustees may let and otherwise manage any property of the Foundation not occupied for the purpose thereof according to the general law applicable to the management of property by Trustees of charitable foundations.' 'The accounts of the Foundation and all books and other documents relating thereto shall be submitted yearly to audit.'

The powers of the Secretary of State for Education and Science relating to this Scheme have since been vested in the Minister for the Arts and the Secretary of State for National Heritage and are now vested in the Secretary of State for Culture, Media and Sport.

Fig. 61: The Master of the 'Mantegna' sketchbook, *c.*1500, folio showing a pilaster strip decorated with foliage and two entablatures from an unknown antique source. The sketchbook may have been produced by a draughtsman at the court of the Gonzaga in Mantua. Pen and ink with grey chalk underdrawing and brown wash *Photograph: Geremy Butler*

APPENDIX IV

ANALYSIS OF THE CONTENTS
OF SIR JOHN SOANE'S MUSEUM

The following analysis is intended to give a general idea of the contents of the Museum in a classified form. It is based on catalogues in MS and many of these figures are provisional. It must be emphasized that such an analysis bears no relation to Soane's attitude to his collection which was personal and empirical, little concerned with chronological classification and still less with 'balanced' representation. It is thought, however, that this summary may be a useful guide to the modern student in search of specific material.

ANCIENT AND MEDIEVAL OBJECTS

EGYPTIAN AND GRÆCO-ROMAN, 38

GREEK AND ROMAN MARBLES

    Architectural Fragments, 130

    Decorative Fragments (Candelabra, Furniture, Ornaments, etc), 99

    Major Frieze and Relief Fragments, 15

    Greek Votive and Funerary Reliefs, 8

    Sarcophagus Fragments, 18

    Cinerary urns, 23

    Funerary Vases, 20

    Statuary: Græco-Roman copies, adaptations, etc., 24

    Statuary: Heads, Busts and Fragments, 33

GREEK AND ROMAN BRONZES, 31

GREEK AND ROMAN TERRACOTTAS, MOSAICS AND MISCELLANEOUS, 47

GREEK AND ROMAN VASES

    East Greek, Attic and Corinthian, 22

    S. Italian, Apulian and Miscellaneous, 37

GEMS

    Egyptian Scarabs, 2

    Greek and Greek Provincial, 3

    Hellenistic, Etruscan, Roman, Early Christian, 160

    Medieval, etc., 4

MEDIEVAL OBJECTS

    Architectural Fragments (mostly from the Old Palace of Westminster), 32

    Objects in Wood, 18

Tiles, Pottery and Glass, 14
Miscellaneous (including a Russo-Greek ivory triptych), 6

RENAISSANCE AND LATER OBJECTS

ITALIAN AND NORTHERN RENAISSANCE BRONZES

Figures, 19
Plaquettes, 5

WORKS BY NAMED ENGLISH SCULPTORS

By John Flaxman (mainly plaster models), 55
By other sculptors, 38

SCULPTURE BASED ON ANTIQUE OR RENAISSANCE MODELS
(MOSTLY PLASTER), 24

MISCELLANEOUS SCULPTURE

Stone and Marble, 7
Alabaster, 8
Terracotta, etc. (including Coade Stone), 24
Plaster (including stucco manufacturers' specimens), 58
Wax, 6

ARCHITECTURAL FRAGMENTS

Stone and Marble (including a few Italian 15th-C. fragments and others from
demolished London buildings), 44
Other materials, 32

MEDALS

Napoleonic, 143
Soane Medal (wax model and various metals), 7
Miscellaneous (mostly late 18th- and early 19th-C.), 16

GEMS

Renaissance and later, 28
Neo-classical, 120
Miscellaneous, 6

ENGRAVED SEALS

Sulphur Casts by N Marchant, 100
Sulphur Casts by E Burch, 100
Miscellaneous, 2

CERAMICS

Maiolica ware, 2
Wedgwood ware, 10
Miscellaneous, 27

This does not include Soane's domestic china

MISCELLANEOUS OBJECTS

Arms, 5

Jewellery (the 'Charles' Jewel, German, early 17th-C.), 1

Timepieces, barometers, etc., 11

Natural Objects, Curiosities, etc., 30

Silver (not including cutlery), 10

16th- and 17th-century stained glass, 99

Unclassified, 45

CASTS

From Antique Buildings, 102

From collections, 105

From Antique and Renaissance originals (sources doubtful or unknown), 235

ORIENTAL AND SOUTH AMERICAN OBJECTS

CHINESE CERAMICS (18th-C.), 42

Chinese export dinner service, 228

Blue and white tiles, Kangxi, 377

MISCELLANEOUS ORIENTAL, 15

PERUVIAN POTTERY, 12

PAINTINGS AND DRAWINGS (excluding architectural drawings)

OIL OR TEMPERA

Italian 16th-C. (Fra Bartolommeo and Cartoon fragment), 2

Italian 17th-C. (Neapolitan), 1

Italian 18th–19th C., 12

French (Watteau), 1

English (18th- and early 19th-C.), 51

Dutch (Cornelis Decker), 1

WATERCOLOUR, BODY-COLOUR, CHALK, PENCIL, ETC

Italian (including 15 by Piranesi), 33

Flemish (including 2 by Ruisdael), 4

Dutch (H Saftleven), 1

French (Clérisseau), 21

Swiss (Lebelle, on silk), 19

English (including 8 by J Cozens), 95

Miscellaneous, 93

MINIATURES
French (Isabey), 1
English (late 18th-C.), 3
ORIENTAL
Volume of Indian miniatures (17th- and 18th-C.), 37

ARCHITECTURAL MODELS

MODELS OF ANTIQUE BUILDINGS
Plaster Models by Fouquet, 20
Cork Models, 14
SOANEAN MODELS
Bank of England, 44
Other Soane Buildings, 57
Miscellaneous, 17
MISCELLANEOUS (including full-size models of ornaments other than casts), 100

ARCHITECTURAL DRAWINGS AND PRINTS

BOUND VOLUMES OF DRAWINGS: ITALIAN
    Drawings by Nicoletto da Modena (early 16th-C.), 68
    Drawings of Roman buildings (so-called 'Codex Coner'; Italian, early 16th-C.), 165
    Drawings by or associated with G Vasari (mid-16th-C.), 213
    Drawings by G B Montano, 3 vols (16th–17th-C.), 333
    Drawings by G B Gisleni (17th-C.), 116
    'Margaret Chinnery' album of miscellaneous 16th-C. drawings, mostly Italian, 76
    Drawings by Carlo Fontana, 2 vols. (18th-C.), 62
    Drawings of Paestum by T Major, 1768, 37
    Various other volumes (6) of drawings, mostly Italian, 398
BOUND VOLUMES OF DRAWINGS: ENGLISH
    Album of John Thorpe (16th–17th-C.), 272
    Drawings by Wren (Greenwich, Hampton Court, etc) and others (17th- and 18th-C.), 229
    Drawings by G Dance the elder (with a few by the younger. See also below), 293
    12 volumes containing drawings principally by the following: R Adam, J Bedford, M Brettingham, E Dodwell, J Nollekens, J Playfair, H Repton, W Reveley, J Rysbrack, G Sampson, T Sandby, P Scheemakers, A Van Assen, 1,635
    Soane Drawings, 37 Voumes, 2,523
    Miscellaneous Engravings in volumes:
    Italy, 40

Collected by G Dance, 128

ADAM COLLECTION, 8,856

SIR W. CHAMBERS COLLECTION, 789

G DANCE COLLECTION, 1,303

SIR JOHN SOANE'S DRAWINGS

Framed drawings (mostly RA exhibits) in Museum, 97

Bank of England, 601

General, 6,266

Lecture Diagrams, 1,080

DRAWINGS BY JAMES PLAYFAIR, 286

MISCELLANEOUS ARCHITECTURAL DRAWINGS, 173

MISCELLANEOUS PRINTS, 758

PENNANT's *London,* extra-illustrated copy from collection of Henry Fauntleroy;
prints and drawings, 1,531

THE LIBRARY

The Library contains 6,857 volumes, more than half of which are books on art,
architecture, topography, etc. There is a small number of MSS and early printed
works, of which the following are most important:

ILLUMINATED MANUSCRIPTS

Biblia Sacra, 13th-C. (English)

Josephus, 15th-C. (Flemish)

Books of Hours:

15th-C. (Flemish)

early 16th-C. (Flemish)

late 15th-C. (Dutch)

15th-C. (French)

Missal 1482 (French)

Le Livre des Cordonniers de Caen, late 15th-C. (French)

Cardinal Marino Grimani's commentary on the Epistle of St Paul to the
Romans with illuminations by Giulio Clovio. Mid-16th-C.

OTHER MANUSCRIPTS

Tasso, Torquato: an early MS of the *Gierusalemme Liberata.*

Francesco di Giorgio Martini: a mid-16th C. version of his Treatise on
Architecture, with marginal drawings.

Stone, Nicholas, the elder: two Account Books, 1631–42.

Stone, Nicholas, the younger: sketch book (France and Italy), 1648.

Stone, Henry: sketch books, 1638.

Newcastle, Margaret Cavendish, Duchess of, *The Second Epistle, an answer and instruction upon six questions, etc.*

Gibbs, James. *A few short cursory remarks on…buildings in Rome,* with biographical fragment.

Bonato, Joseph Antonio: *Catalogus Plantarum quae in Horto Botanico Regii Archilycei Patavini anno MDCCCIX vigerunt,* 1809 (A MS belonging to the Empress Josephine and from the Library at Malmaison. It was bought by Soane in 1823.)

Reynolds, Sir Joshua: a sketch book containing drawings made in Rome.

EARLY PRINTED BOOKS

Landino, C, *Commentario.…sopra la Comedia di Danthe,* 1481

Brant, S *Stultifera Navis,* 1488

Boetius, *De Philosophico Consolatu,* 1501

Cuba, J W von, *Ortus Sanitatis,* 1517

Portiforium seu Breviarum ad Sarisburiensis ecclesiae usum, 1555

Shakespeare, W, *Comedies, Histories and Tragedies,* fol. 1623

FURNITURE

Most of the furniture in the Museum was acquired by Soane for the general furnishing of his establishment. It is for the most part of good domestic quality of a standard kind, although some pieces would seem to have been specially commissioned, some to designs by Soane himself. Only a few items were acquired for their antiquarian interest and these are mentioned in the text. Thus 16 items date from before 1750, 98 from the latter part of the 18th or early part of the 19th century, and 10 from shortly after the time of Soane's death when the first Curator required furnishings for his apartment.

APPENDIX V

INVENTORIES AND CATALOGUES

Works of Art

The basic document is the manuscript Inventory prepared by the first Curator, George Bailey. He began work in 1835 and several drafts survive. His final completed version is dated January 1837. This covers: works of art, natural curiosities; stained glass; paintings, drawings and engravings in frames; contents of drawers and cases; furniture and fittings. There are 4 copies of this first inventory, all with informative annotations. Bailey compiled a further inventory of paintings, drawings and prints in frames and some not in frames, in 1840, showing rearrangements at that date.

No new inventories were made until the appointment as Curator of Walter L Spiers in 1904. Spiers compiled a thorough annotated inventory (MS) of objects of art (excluding paintings etc.), based on Bailey but with diagrams showing the positions of all objects in 1905. Revised versions of these diagrams are in current use. Spiers also compiled an inventory of paintings, drawings and engravings in frames, architectural drawings and engravings in drawers and cabinets, as arranged in 1907. This also includes an inventory of stained glass, which records for the first time the subjects of the panels.

The Egyptian antiquities were catalogued by Dr Margaret A Murray in 1946. The Classical antiquities and the antique and neo-classical gems were catalogued by Dr Cornelius Vermeule in 1951–53, his catalogue incorporating Dr Murray's entries for the Egyptian items. The catalogue was issued in a limited edition of typescript copies in Boston, USA, 1975.

A catalogue (MS) of sculpture (excluding casts) and a card index of the entire collection under typological headings were compiled by Sir John Summerson during his curatorship. A catalogue of models of Sir John Soane's works, compiled by Dr John Wilton-Ely, was published in *Architectural History*, xii (1969), pp.5–38, Figs 1–21.

Peter Thornton initiated the compiling of catalogue sheets for every object, piece of furniture and framed item (painting, engraving etc.) in 1985. This task is now complete. Esther Caplin has classified and sorted the works of art into typological categories and Helen Dorey has sorted the paintings etc. into categories by artist. The manuscript catalogue of Soane's models, compiled by Finch Allibone in 1988 has been incorporated into the Architectural Models category.

The Research Library

The earliest extant inventory of the Library is by C J Richardson, dated 1831, and includes plans showing the location of bookcases. It is in manuscript with annotations by Bailey and Soane himself. A manuscript catalogue was compiled by George Bailey in 1837 and he also prepared a shelf-list of the library, as arranged in 1854. Bailey also compiled a subject index (MS, 2 vols, undated) classified under 22 headings. *A Catalogue of the Original Drawings and Printed Books on Art and Science in* . . . *Sir John Soane's Museum* was printed and published by Shaw and Sons, Fetter Lane, in 1844. This highly selective work was superseded by a *Catalogue of the Library in Sir John Soane's Museum,* printed for the Trustees in 1878. This, prepared by a Mr W A Cooper, was considered by the Trustees to be not sufficiently accurate for general distribution. Only 26 copies were bound.

In 1905, Walter. L Spiers compiled a manuscript inventory of the books as shelved in that year, with marginal notes on bindings, insertions, book-plates etc. This was followed in 1906 by catalogues of views and portraits in the interleaved 'Fauntleroy' Pennant and Evelyn's Diary and in 1907 by an inventory of drawings bound up in volumes. In 1908 Spiers produced a topographical catalogue covering the entire collection of drawings and a limited number of printed works. In 1909, he completed a manuscript catalogue with indices, of the 54 volumes of drawings by Robert and James Adam. This, topographically arranged, was printed in A T Bolton, *The Architecture of Robert and James Adam* 1922, Vol.ii, and reprinted in W L Spiers, *Catalogue of the Drawings and Designs by Robert and James Adam* (Chadwyck-Healey, Cambridge and Somerset House, Tenneck, N J) 1979, together with Spiers' inventories of the several volumes.

On the re-organization of the library in 1924 in two sections, by Arthur T Bolton, separate manuscript catalogues of the general library (ground floor) and architectural library (first floor) were compiled and these are now in current use. The architectural drawings were re-catalogued at the same date, with an index (typescript).

Catalogues of special sections of the library, not included in the above, are as follows: catalogue (MS) of III volumes of Pamphlets, with index, compiled by G Northover, 1925; Index (MS) of Sale Catalogues, Publishers' and Booksellers' Lists etc., not dated; Catalogue (typescript) of the Private Correspondence of Sir John Soane, compiled by Arthur T Bolton. Printed catalogues and descriptions include E G Millar, 'Les Manuscrits. . . de la Bibliothéque du Musée de Sir John Soane', *Les Manuscrits a Peinture des Bibliothéques de Londres,* Paris 1914–20; W L Spiers, *The Note-book and Accounts Book of Nicholas Stone,* Walpole Society, vii, 1919; J Summerson, *The Book of Architecture of John Thorpe,* Walpole Society, xi, 1966.

A commercial microfilm of the architectural and decorative drawings in the collection together with a concise catalogue has been prepared. (Microfilm and a printed hand list of the collection of drawings by Robert Adam and his Office have already been published). These microfilms are available from ProQuest Information and Learning (formerly Chadwyck-Healey Ltd), The Quorum, Barnwell Road, Cambridge CB5 8SW. Copies may be consulted in the Museum's Research Library (it is necessary to make an appointment). The concise catalogue is available via the Museum's website (www.soane.org).

A new integrated online catalogue of both libraries will be published incrementally on the Museum's website (www.soane.org) from 2007.

A catalogue of the Renaissance drawings in the collection was published in 1998: Lynda Fairbairn *Italian Renaissance Drawings from the Collection of Sir John Soane's Museum* 2 vols, Azimuth Editions.

A *Catalogue of the Drawings of George Dance the Younger (1741–1825) and of George Dance the Elder (1695–1768) from the Collection of Sir John Soane's Museum* by Jill Lever was published by Azimuth Editions in 2003.

From 2007 catalogues of drawings in the collection will be published online on the Museum's website (www.soane.org). First to appear will be a catalogue of the Baroque Drawings by Dr Gordon Higgott. This will be followed by a catalogue of the first section of the Adam collection (The Grand Tour drawings of Robert and James Adam) by Professor Alan Tait and the first section of drawings by Soane himself (1770–80) by Jill Lever.

Fig. 62: Unexecuted design for a Mausoleum for Frederick, Prince of Wales, to be built in Kew Gardens, Surrey, by Sir William Chambers, 1751. Pencil, pen and watercolour. *Photograph: Geremy Butler*

APPENDIX VI

SELECT BIBLIOGRAPHY

The first biography of Soane was John Britton's *A Brief Memoir of Sir John Soane*, published in 1834, three years before the architect's death. This was followed by Soane's own account of his life, *Memoirs of the Professional Life of an Architect*, privately printed in 1835. Then in 1837, immediately following Soane's death, came T L Donaldson's *Review of the Professional Life of Sir John Soane*. No further biographical works were published in the nineteenth century, apart from notices in biographical dictionaries.

Interest in Soane revived in the nineteen-twenties and in 1927 *The Portrait of Sir John Soane*, a collection of letters arranged and annotated to illustrate episodes in his career, was published under the editorship of Arthur T Bolton (Curator 1917–45). Bolton also edited the *Lectures on Architecture* (1925) and wrote *The Works of Sir John Soane* (1924), *Architectural Education a Century Ago* (*c.*1923) and *English Sculptures of the 18th century in the Sir John Joane Museum* (1924). He also published, in 1933, *A short Account of the Evolution of the Tivoli Corner of the Bank of England, designed by Sir John Soane, R.A., 1804–5. Issued by the Trustees of the Sir John Soane's Museum as a protest againts any alteration of the Design and as a record*. H J Birnstingl's *Sir John Soane* (1925) is a short essay with photographs of Soane's work by F R Yerbury. Photographs by Yerbury also constitute the main part of H R Steele and F R Yerbury, *The Old Bank of England*, a record of Soane's largely demolished work, published in 1930.

Since 1930 the following books have appeared on Soane and the Museum:

J Summerson, *Sir John Soane*, 1952. A brief critical essay with illustrations.

D Stroud, *The Architecture of Sir John Soane*, 1961. Introduction by H R Hitchcock.

P de la Ruffinière du Prey, *John Soane; the making of an Architect*, 1982. A detailed and fully-illustrated account of the first thirty years of Soane's life.

John Soane. Academy Editions Monograph, 1983. Illustrations include many colour reproductions of drawings in the Museum. Essays by John Summerson, David Watkin and G Tilman Mellinghoff.

D Stroud, *Sir John Soane, Architect,* 1984. Supersedes the same author's book of 1961 and contains a biography and *catalogue raisonné* of works.

P de la Ruffinière du Prey, *Sir John Soane*. Architectural drawings in the Victoria and Albert Museum, London, 1985.

Susan Feinberg Millenson, *Sir John Soane's Museum*, UMI Research Press, 1987. Published version of a PhD thesis on the origins and evolution of Soane's Museum.

Eva Schumann-Bacia, *Die Bank von England,* Artemis and Winkler, 1989. (English translation *John Soane and The Bank of England* published by Longman, London and New York, 1991).

Soane and After: The Architecture of Dulwich Picture Gallery, Exhibition Catalogue, London, 1987.

Christina Scull, *The Soane Hogarths,* Trefoil Publications, London, 1991; revised edition 2007.

Peter Thornton and Helen Dorey, *A Miscellany of Objects from Sir John Soane's Museum,* London, 1992.

Stefan Buzas, *Sir John Soane's Museum, London,* Wasmuth, 1994.

Soane: Connoisseur and Collector, Exhibition Catalogue, Sir John Soane's Museum, London, 1995.

Buildings in Progress: Soane's Views of Construction, Exhibition Catalogue, Sir John Soane's Museum, London, 1995.

Soane Revisited: A Journey of Rediscovery of the Buildings of Sir John Soane, Exhibition Catalogue, Sir John Soane's Museum, London 1996.

Giles Waterfield (ed.), *Soane and Death,* Exhibition Catalogue, Dulwich Picture Gallery, 1996.

Robert Adam: The Creative Mind: from the sketch to the finished drawing, Exhibition Catalogue, Sir John Soane's Museum, London, 1996.

David Watkin, *Sir John Soane: Enlightenment Thought and the Royal Academy Lectures,* Cambridge, 1996.

David Watkin, *Sir John Soane and Enlightenment Thought:* The Annual Soane Lecture, 1996.

Dorothy Stroud, *Sir John Soane Architect,* second revised edition, De La Mare Publishers Ltd, 1996.

Robin Simon & Christopher Woodward (eds), *A Rake's Progress: From Hogarth to Hockney,* Exhibition Catalogue, Sir John Soane's Museum 1997.

Susan Palmer, *The Soanes at Home: Domestic Life at Lincoln's Inn Fields,* London 1998, reprinted with corrections 2002.

Lynda Fairbairn, *Italian Renaissance Drawings from the Collection of Sir John Soane's Museum,* Azimuth Editions, 1998.

Lynda Fairbairn, *The North Italian Album,* Azimuth Editions, 1998.

J G Links, *The Soane Canalettos,* Azimuth Editions, 1998.

Visions of Ruin: Architectural fantasies and designs for garden follies, Exhibition Catalogue incorporating *Crude Hints towards a History of my House,* (ed. Helen Dorey), Sir John Soane's Museum, London 1999.

Inspired by Soane, Exhibition Catalogue, Sir John Soane's Museum, 1999.

Gillian Darley, *John Soane: An Accidental Romantic*, Yale University Press, London and New Haven, 1999 (revised edition published in paperback, 2000).

Ptolemy Dean, *Sir John Soane and the Country Estate*, London, 1999.

Margaret Richardson and MaryAnne Stevens (eds), *John Soane: Master of Space and Light*, Exhibition Catalogue, Royal Academy publications, 1999.

David Watkin (ed.), *Sir John Soane: The Royal Academy Lectures*, Cambridge, 2000.

Sean Sawyer, *Soane at Westminster: Civic Architecture and National Identity, 1789–1834*, PhD thesis, Columbia University, 1999.

Charles Jencks, *The Riddle of John Soane: Deciphering the enigma code of Soanic architecture*, The Annual Soane Lecture 1999.

Stephen Astley, *Robert Adam's Castles*, Exhibition Catalogue, Sir John Soane's Museum, London 2000.

Francesco Nevola, *Soane's Favourite Subject: The Story of Dulwich Picture Gallery*, London 2000.

Ruth Guilding, *Marble Mania: sculpture galleries in England 1640–1840*, Exhibition Catalogue, Sir John Soane's Museum, London 2001.

David Bindman, David Ekserdjian & William Palin (eds), *Hogarth's Election Entertainment: Artists at the Hustings*, Exhibition Catalogue, Sir John Soane's Museum, London 2001.

Brian Lukacher, *Joseph Gandy in the Shadow of the Enlightenment*, The Annual Soane Lecture 2001.

Eileen Harris, *The Genius of Robert Adam His Interiors*, London 2001.

John Wilton-Ely, *Piranesi, Paestum and Soane*, Azimuth Editions, 2002.

Terrance Galvin, *The Architecture of Joseph Michael Gandy (1771–1843) and Sir John Soane (1753–1837): An Exploration into the Masonic and Occult Imagination of the late Enlightenment*, PhD thesis, University of Pennsylvania, 2003.

Angelo Maggi & Nicola Navone (eds), *John Soane and the Wooden Bridges of Switzerland: architecture and the culture of technology from Palladio to the Grubenmanns*, Mendrisio 2003.

Jill Lever, *Catalogue of the Drawings of George Dance the Younger (1741–1825) and of George Dance the Elder (1695–1768) from the collection of Sir John Soane's Museum*, Azimuth Editions, 2003.

Alistair Rowan, *'Bob the Roman': Heroic Antiquity & the Architecture of Robert Adam*, Exhibition Catalogue, Sir John Soane's Museum, London 2003.

David Bindman (ed.), *Flaxman: Master of the Purest Line*, Exhibition Catalogue, Sir John Soane's Museum, London 2003.

Sandra Coley (ed.), *The Stained Glass Collection of Sir John Soane's Museum. The Journal of Stained Glass* Vol.XXVII, 2004.

William Palin (ed.), *Saving Wotton: The Remarkable Story of a Soane Country House*, Exhibition Catalogue, Sir John Soane's Museum, London 2004.

Eileen Harris and Nick Savage (eds), *Hooked on Books: The Library of Sir John Soane*, Exhibition Catalogue, Sir John Soane's Museum, London 2004.

Jill Lever, *'Architecture Unshackled': George Dance the Younger 1741–1825*, Exhibition Guide, Sir John Soane's Museum, London 2004.

Murray Grigor (director), *John Soane: An English Architect, An American Legacy*, A Checkerboard Film Production, DVD, New York 2004.

Julius Bryant (ed.), *Thomas Banks (1735–1805): Britain's First Modern Sculptor*, Exhibition Catalogue, Sir John Soane's Museum, London 2005.

Daniel Abramson, *Building the Bank of England: Money, Architecture, Society*, New Haven and London, 2005.

Ptolemy Dean, *Sir John Soane and London*, Aldershot, 2006.

Christopher Woodward, *Soane's Magician: the Tragic Genius of Joseph Michael Gandy*, Exhibition Guide, Sir John Soane's Museum, London 2006.

Brian Lukacher, *Joseph Gandy An Architectural Visionary in Georgian England*, London 2006.

Helen Dorey, *John Soane and J M W Turner: Illuminating a Friendship*, Exhibition Catalogue, Sir John Soane's Museum, London 2007.

David Watkin, *Visions of World Architecture: John Soane's Royal Academy Lecture Illustrations*, Exhibition Guide, Sir John Soane's Museum, London 2007.

The following major articles on Soane and the Museum have also appeared.

John Summerson, 'Sir John Soane', *The Times*, 20 January 1937.

John Summerson, 'The Subtle Magic of Sir John Soane', *The Listener*, 11 September 1947.

John Summerson 'Change, Decay and the Soane Museum', *Architectural Association Journal*, October 1949.

John Summerson, 'Soane: The Case History of a Personal Style', *RIBA Journal*, 3rd Series, LVIII, 1951.

Cornelius Vermeule, 'Sir John Soane, His Classical Antiquities', *Archaeology* 6, 1953.

Dorothy Stroud, 'The Early Work of Soane', *Architectural Review*, February 1957.

John Wilton-Ely, 'The Architectural Models of Sir John Soane: A Catalogue', *Architectural History*, Vol.12, 1969.

John Summerson 'Sir John Soane and the Furniture of Death', *Architectural Review*, March 1978.

John Summerson, 'The Union of the Arts', *Lotus International*, 35, 1982 II.

Richard Lorch, 'The Architectural Order of Sir John Soane's House', *International Architect*, vol.2, no.9, 1982.

Susan Feinberg, 'The Genesis of Sir John Soane's Museum Idea: 1801–1810', *Journal of the Society of Architectural Historians*, vol. 43, October 1984.

Ilse Trechsel 'Das Soane Haus in London', *Künstler Häuser*, Editor Eduard Huttinger, Zurich and Munich. *c.*1984.

Peter Thornton 'Lit up with Gorgeous Hues'. *Country Life*, 19 December 1985.

Peter Thornton 'An architectural kaleidoscope: Sir John Soane's Museum in London', *The Magazine Antiques*, New York, January 1987.

Brian Lukacher, 'John Soane and his draughtsman Joseph Michael Gandy', *Daidalos*, vol.25, September 1987.

Dan Cruickshank, 'Soane and the Meaning of Colour', *Architectural Review*, vol. 185, January 1989.

Margaret Richardson 'Model Architecture', *Country Life*, 21 September 1989.

Apollo, April 1990: a special Soane Museum issue with articles by Peter Thornton 'The Soane As It Was', Margaret Richardson 'Soane's Use of Drawings', Susan Palmer 'The Papers of Sir John Soane' and Eileen Harris 'Sir John Soane's Library'.

John Summerson 'Sir John Soane and the Furniture of Death' and 'The Evolution of Soane's Bank Stock Office' are included in *The Unromantic Castle and Other Essays*, 1990.

John Summerson, 'The Evolution of Soane's Bank Stock Office' is also among the articles in *Design and Practice in British Architecture: Studies in Architectural History presented to Howard Colvin;* Architectural History Volume 27, 1984.

Margaret Richardson, 'John Soane; The Business of Architecture', in *Georgian Architectural Practice*, The Georgian Group Symposium 1991, London, 1991.

Margaret Richardson, 'Learning in the Soane Office', in Bingham, Neil (ed), *The Education of the Architect, Proceedings of the 22nd Annual Symposium of the Society of Architectural Historians of Great Britain*, London, 1992.

Helen Dorey, 'Sir John Soane's Acquisition of the Sarcophagus of Seti I', *Georgian Group Journal*, 1991.

Anthony Jackson, 'The Facade of Sir John Soane's Museum: a Study in Contextualism', *Journal of the Society of Architectural Historians*, vol.51, December 1992.

John Elsner, 'A Collector's Model of Desire: The House and Museum of Sir John Soane', *The Culture of Collecting*, London 1993.

Todd Wilmert, 'Heating Methods and Their Impact on Soane's Work: Lincoln's Inn Fields and Dulwich Picture Gallery', *Journal of the Society of Architectural Historians*, Vol. LII No. 1, March 1993.

David Watkin, 'Freemasonry and Sir John Soane', *Journal of the Society of Architectural Historians*, 54:4, December 1995.

Richard Hewlings, '11 Downing Street: John Soane's Work for John Eliot (1797–1805)', *Transactions of the Ancient Monument Society* Vol. 39, 1995.

Sean Sawyer, 'Sir John Soane's Symbolic Westminster: The Apotheosis of George IV', Architectural History Vol.39, 1996.

Helen Dorey, 'The Historic Framing and presentation of watercolours, drawings and prints at Sir John Soane's Museum', *The Historic Framing and Presentation of Watercolours, Drawings and Prints* ed. Nancy Bell, 1997.

Peter Mutran & Thomas Gluck, 'Sir John Soane's House and Musuem Model', *arq*, Vol.2, Summer 1997.

Helene Furján, 'The Specular Spectacle of the House of the Collector', *Assemblage* 34, 1997.

Christopher Woodward, 'William Beckford and Fonthill Splendens: Early Works by Soane and Goodridge', *Apollo*, Feb. 1998.

Laurence Kinney, 'John Soane and Property: The Argyle Rooms and All Souls College, Oxford, two case studies', *Architectural History* Vol. 41: 1998.

Richard Garnier, 'Downing Square in the 1770s and 1780s', *The Georgian Group Journal* Vol. IX. 1999.

Roger Bowdler & Christopher Woodward, ' "An Ornamental Structure and Very Likely to be Damaged …": Sir John Soane's Tomb in St Pancras Gardens, London', *Architectural History* Vol. 42, 1999.

Christopher Woodward, 'Dancing Soane. The Yellow Drawing Room at Wimpole Hall', *Apollo*, April 1999.

Helen Dorey, 'Sir John Soane's Courtyard Gardens at Lincoln's Inn Fields' *The London Gardener*, 1999–2000.

Sean Sawyer, 'Sir John Soane and the Late Georgian Origins of the Royal Entrance', Christine and Jacqueline Riding (eds), *The Houses of Parliament: History, Art, Architecture*, London 2000.

Christopher Evans, 'Megalithic Follies: Soane's "Druidic Remains" and the Display of Monuments', *Journal of Material Culture* Vol.5 (3), 2000.

Robin Middleton, 'The Magpie of Lincoln's Inn Fields', *Architecture and Ideas*, Winter/Spring 2001.

Pierre de la Ruffinière du Prey, 'Soane Drawings – A Laying on of Hands', *Architecture and Ideas*, Winter/Spring 2001.

Ian Goodall and Margaret Richardson, 'A Recently Discovered Gandy Sketchbook', *Architectural History* Vol. 44, 2001.

Helene Furján, 'Sir John Soane's Spectacular Theatre', *AA Files* 47, [2001].

Jaś Elsner, 'Architecture, Antiquarianism and Archaeology in Sir John Soane's Museum', Athena Tsingarida & Donna Kurtz (eds), *Appropriating Antiquity/ Saisir l'Antique: Collections et collectionneurs d'antiques en Belgique et en Grand-Bretagne au XIXe siècle*, Brussels 2002.

Gillian Darley, 'The Surprising Discretion of Soane and Repton', *The Georgian Group Journal* Vol. XII, 2002.

Rose Kerr, 'Hidden Treasures at Sir John Soane's Museum', *Apollo*, Nov. 2002.

Helen Dorey, 'Sir John Soane's Museum', *Minerva* 19, Nov./Dec. 2002.

Bianca de Divitiis, 'A newly discovered volume from the office of Sir John Soane', *The Burlington Magazine* CXLV, March 2003.

David Adshead, ' "Like a Roman sepulchre" : John Soane's design for a *Castello d'acqua* at Wimpole, Cambridgeshire, and its Italian origins', *Apollo*, April 2003.

Timothy Brittain-Caitlin, 'Unseen Soane', *The World of Interiors*, September 2003.

David Yeomans, 'Soane and Swiss Bridges', *Construction History* Vol. 19, 2003.

Margaret Richardson, 'John Soane and the Temple of Vesta at Tivoli', *Architectural History* Vol. 46, 2003.

Gavin Stamp, 'Soane in Glasgow', *The Georgian Group Journal* Vol. XIII, 2003.

Susan Palmer, 'Sir John Soane's Garden at the Royal Hospital Chelsea', *The London Gardener* Vol.9, 2003–04.

Helen Dorey, 'Sir John Soane's Pitzhanger', *Trackers*, Exhibition Catalogue, Pitzhanger Manor, Ealing, 2004.

Bianca de Divitiis, 'Plans, Elevations and Perspective Views of Pitzhanger Manor-House', *The Georgian Group Journal* Vol. XIV, 2004.

Peter Inskip, 'Moggerhanger', *The Georgian Group Journal* Vol. XIV, 2004.

Bianca de Divitiis, 'New Drawings for the Interiors of the Breakfast Room and Library at Pitzhanger Manor', *Architectural History* Vol. 48, 2005.

Susan Palmer, 'Sir John Soane and the Design of the New State Paper Office, 1829–1834', *Archivaria* 60, 2006.

Sean Sawyer, 'Order out of Chaos: Soane's Law Courts as a Paradigm for Architecture in the Age of Historicism', Barry Bergdoll & Werner Oechslin (eds), *Fragments Architecture and the Unfinished: Essays Presented to Robin Middleton*, London 2006.

Edward Wendt, 'Soane, Turner and the Matter of Fragmentation', Barry Bergdoll & Werner Oechslin (eds), *Fragments Architecture and the Unfinished: Essays Presented to Robin Middleton*, London 2006.

APPENDIX VII

OTHER SOANE BUILDINGS READILY ACCESSIBLE
TO THE PUBLIC

London Area

The Bank of England. Soane's principal achievement. Considerably altered in 1920s but exterior wall largely preserved. The Bank of England Museum (opened in 1988) includes a re-creation of Soane's Bank Stock Office. Open Monday–Friday, 10am–5pm. Closed Public and Bank Holidays. Tel. 020 7601 5545. www.bankofengland.co.uk

The Royal Hospital, Chelsea. Secretary's Office and Stables. Stables visible from Royal Hospital Road. The Secretary's Office is now a Museum open 10–12am, 2–4pm Monday–Saturday, and Sundays from April–September, 2–4pm. Tel. 020 7730 0161. www.chelsea-pensioners.co.uk

Loutherbourg tomb, Chiswick. In the churchyard of St Nicholas.

The Dulwich Picture Gallery. College Road, Dulwich Village. England's oldest public art gallery, built by Soane 1811–12 to house the picture collection and mausoleum of Soane's close friend, Sir Francis Bourgeois. Open Tuesday–Friday, 10am–5pm. Weekends and Bank Holiday Mondays, 11am–5pm. Closed Mondays except Bank Holidays. Tel. 020 8693 5254. www.dulwichpicturegallery.org.uk

Norwood Hall, Norwood. Visible from Norwood Green Road. Now privately owned.

Pembroke Lodge, Richmond Park. Soane's trellis room is now part of the Tea Rooms but has lost its decoration. Tel. 020 8940 8207. www.pembroke-lodge.co.uk

Pitzhanger Manor, Ealing. Soane's country villa, recently restored and now open to the public. Tuesday–Friday, 1pm–5pm. Saturday 11am–5pm. Tel. 020 8567 1227 www.ealing.gov.uk/pmgalleryandhouse

The Soane Family Tomb. St Pancras Gardens (Old St Pancras churchyard, Pancras Road).

Holy Trinity Church, Marylebone. Exterior visible from the Marylebone Road opposite Gt Portland St tube station.

St John's Church, Bethnal Green. Currently undergoing restoration. Open during Sunday services only.

St Mary Abbot's, Kensington. Soane designed Miss Elizabeth Johnstone's tomb in the churchyard.

St Peter's Church, Walworth.

Southwark Cathedral. Soane designed the Newland Memorial tablet.

Other Cities

Norwich, Blackfriars Bridge.

Reading, Market Place, Simeon Monument.

Solihull, 936 Warwick Road. Barn of Doric form (Barn à la Paestum). Private house, visible from road.

Winchester, Hyde Close. The Reverend Mr Richard's Academy. Visible from road.

Country Houses

Aynhoe Park, Aynho, Northamptonshire (1799). (6 miles SE of Banbury on the London–Birmingham road). Additions by Soane. Private. Entrance façade visible from public road.

Bramley, Hampshire. Soane designed the Brocas memorial chapel in the Church of St James.

Chillington Hall, nr Wolverhampton (1785). Open Thursday and Sunday in July, and Wednesday, Thursday, Friday and Sunday in August. Also open Easter Sunday, May Bank Holiday Sunday and the Sunday of the late spring Bank Holiday (end of May) 2–5pm. Other times by appointment. Tel. 01902 850 236. www.chillingtonhall.co.uk

Hamels Park, Hertfordshire. Now the East Herts. Golf Club. 1.5 miles WSW of Braughing. Two lodges built by Soane can be seen at the entrance on the public road.

Langley Park, Norfolk. Now the Langley School. (Chedgrave–Thurton Road leading off A146). Gateway and two sets of lodges, visible from the public road.

Moggerhanger House, The Park, Moggerhanger, Bedfordshire. House now in the care of Moggerhanger House Preservation Trust. Recently restored and now a Christian conference centre. Restoration of the Repton park is on-going. Open to the public for organised tours throughout the summer. Restaurant and Tea Rooms. Tel. 01767 641 007. www.the-park.net/moggerhangerpark

Saxlingham Rectory, Norfolk. The rectory is visible from the churchyard.

Pellwall, Shropshire. Private. (A529 Market Drayton–Newport road). The triangular lodge can be seen from the public road and the house can be glimpsed from the same road. Currently undergoing restoration. The exterior walls and roofs have been rebuilt and Victorian additions demolished.

Tyringham, Buckinghamshire. Private. Gateway and bridge are on the public road (B526). The house can be seen from the same road.

Wardour Castle, Wiltshire. Additions to the Chapel by Soane. Chapel open for Mass 10.30am Sunday and 9.15am Tuesday. The Chapel can also be visited by arrangement with Lord Talbot of Malahide, Hook Manor, Donhead St Andrew, Shaftesbury, Dorset.

Wimpole Hall, Cambridgeshire. Drawing Room, Library, plunge bath and farm buildings by Soane, 1790. Now a National Trust property. Opening times for hall and farm: see website at www.wimpole.org. Tel. 01223 206 000 Fax 01223 207 838. wimpolehall@nationaltrust.org.uk

Houses Altered/Extended

1783   Burnham Westgate Hall, Norfolk. Private.

1783   Malvern Hall, Warwickshire. Private school.

1786   Ryston Hall, Norfolk. Private.

1788   Bentley Priory, Stanmore.

1804   Port Eliot, Cornwall. Private.

1804   Ramsey Abbey, Cambridgeshire. School Study Centre.

1805   Stowe, Buckinghamshire. Gothic library. School.

1818   Marden Hill, Hertfordshire. Private house.

For a complete list of executed works by Soane, see John Soane Architect *(eds Margaret Richardson and MaryAnne Stevens), Royal Academy Publications, 1999* or contact the Museum's Research Library on 020 7440 4251 for further information.

Fig 63: The façade of Moggerhanger House, Bedfordshire, after restoration 2001

INDEX

Note: Page numbers in **bold** type refer to illustrations. Sir John Soane is referred to in the index by initials JS.

GENERAL REGULATIONS

1 The Museum is open free from Tuesday to Saturday inclusive, from 10am to 5 pm. It is also open on the first Tuesday evening in each month from 6 pm to 9 pm (a charge is made for the evening opening). It is closed on Sundays, Mondays, Bank Holidays and Christmas Eve.

2 Each person, or one in the case of a party, is required to sign his or her name and address in the Visitor's Book.

3 All groups (more than 6 people) must book in advance (telephone 020 7440 4263). Groups are not accepted on Saturdays or on the first Tuesday of the month for the evening opening.

4 Sticks, umbrellas, rucksacks, cases and parcels or large handbags must be left with the attendant in the Entrance Hall. The Museum reserves the right to refuse large bags and items are left at the owner's own risk.

5 Books, drawings, and archives may be consulted between 10 am and 1 pm and 2 pm and 5 pm Tuesday to Friday. The Libary is also open for half a day on Saturday (please consult staff for details). An appointment should be made in advance with the Research Library. Telephone 020 7440 4251.

6 Sketching is permitted in the Museum provided that circulation is not impeded by the sketcher or his equipment. Inks, paints and charcoal are not permitted. For making measured drawings permission must be obtained from the Director.

7 Photography is not permitted. Students may be permitted to photograph if arrangements have been made in advance, in writing (students must produce appropriate identification). Flash, tripods, etc. cannot be used without permission.

8 Photographs of the interiors, paintings or other objects in the Museum may not be published without permission from the Director. To order photographs of the Museum or its works of art please contact Susan Palmer (telephone 020 7440 4245 or spalmer@soane.org.uk).

9 Visitors are not permitted to smoke or partake of refreshment in the Museum.

10 Mobile phones should not be used in the Museum.

11 Children under the age of 12 will not be admitted unless in the charge of a responsible adult.

12 Perambulators, pushchairs, etc., may not be brought into the Museum. The Museum has two specially made wheelchairs available for use by visitors: please call 020 7440 4263 in advance for assistance.

Telephone: 020 7405 2107
Facsimile: 020 7831 3957
Website: www.soane.org